ESCAPE ROOM PUZZLES

Published in 2018 by Welbeck
an imprint of Welbeck Non-Fiction,
part of Welbeck Publishing Group
20 Mortimer Street, London W1T 3JW

10 8 6 5 7 9

A CIP catalogue for this book is available from the British Library.

ISBN 978-1-78177-904-0

Design: RockJaw Creative
Managing Art Editor: Luke Griffin
Editor: Chris Mitchell

Printed in Dubai

Welbeck Publishing Group apologises for any unintentional errors or omissions that will
be corrected in future editions of this book.

INTRODUCTION

This book is, most likely, different to any other puzzle book you've encountered.

Most puzzle books are orderly affairs. Regular structuring. Clearly defined problems. Compact — if difficult — challenges. In other words, they're safe. This is a very different beast. To get anywhere with *Escape Room Puzzles*, you need to approach the book one section at a time.

Some chapters have more than one section, and each one is a puzzle made up of interlocking pieces. Some sections hinge on knowledge you acquired earlier on, while others are entirely self-contained. To help Adam, a young reporter and our plucky hero, and his friend Henry through the trials inside this book, you'll often need to think outside the box.

The way to approach a section is to read it through, letting Adam show you the things he considers to be of importance. You'll know when you come to the end of the section, because he'll always make it clear that he needs to come up with an answer BEFORE HE CAN PROCEED. Do not read on — the answer may be revealed on the next page!

Once you've read over the section, go back and look at it again. On this second pass, you'll know what it is you need to end up with — whether it's a word, or a number of so many digits, or a certain pattern. The puzzles you have to solve in each section will stand out, but exactly how to combine them, or what order to start in, may be less obvious.

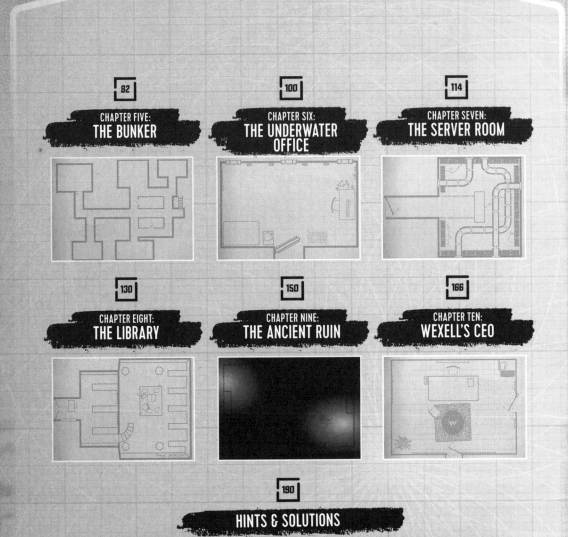

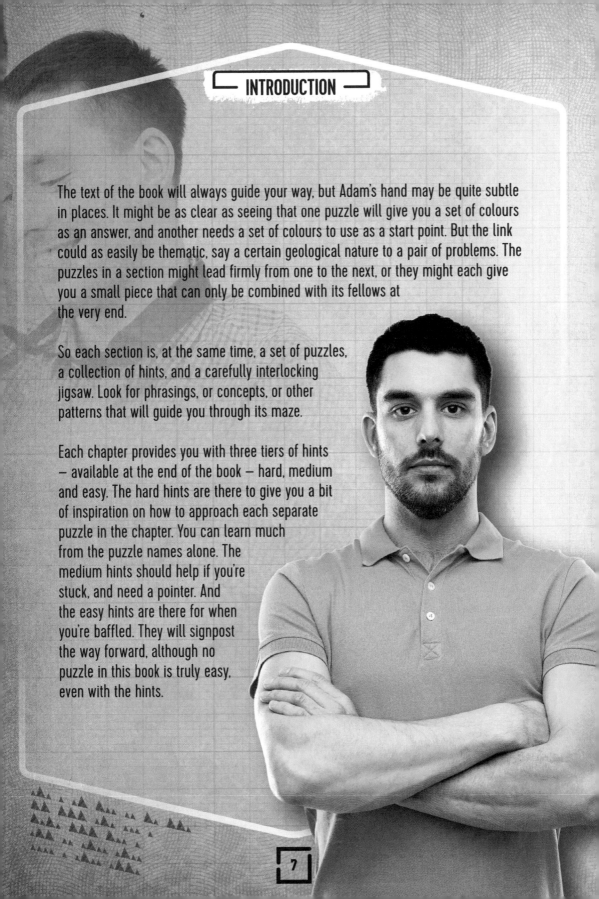

INTRODUCTION

The text of the book will always guide your way, but Adam's hand may be quite subtle in places. It might be as clear as seeing that one puzzle will give you a set of colours as an answer, and another needs a set of colours to use as a start point. But the link could as easily be thematic, say a certain geological nature to a pair of problems. The puzzles in a section might lead firmly from one to the next, or they might each give you a small piece that can only be combined with its fellows at the very end.

So each section is, at the same time, a set of puzzles, a collection of hints, and a carefully interlocking jigsaw. Look for phrasings, or concepts, or other patterns that will guide you through its maze.

Each chapter provides you with three tiers of hints — available at the end of the book — hard, medium and easy. The hard hints are there to give you a bit of inspiration on how to approach each separate puzzle in the chapter. You can learn much from the puzzle names alone. The medium hints should help if you're stuck, and need a pointer. And the easy hints are there for when you're baffled. They will signpost the way forward, although no puzzle in this book is truly easy, even with the hints.

One final note: some puzzles will need physical manipulation to solve. When you see the scissors icon and dotted lines, you're probably going to want to cut things out and turn them into 2D or 3D shapes. Some of these might be needed later in the book, so keep everything you have cut out until you complete the book. If you don't want to damage the book, these pages can be photocopied, photographed and printed, or even traced over. If you're a spatial awareness genius, you might even be able to do it all in your head!

GOOD LUCK!

CONTENTS

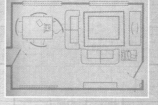
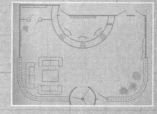

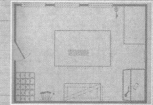

ESCAPE ROOM PUZZLES

JAMES HAMER-MORTON
Creator of Deadlocked Escape Rooms

WELBECK

NOTE FROM THE AUTHOR

Escape Rooms are a growing industry, still exploding into the mainstream and finding their feet. Originally designed as a series of keys and locks, companies are experimenting to create unique rooms relevant to modern zeitgeists. Deadlocked Rooms decided to step away from padlocks, while remaining as diegetic and realistic as possible.

One of our Deadlocked rooms involved a series of puzzles that used documents and articles that, when referenced together, led to something else entirely. A chance encounter with a publisher — and an invite to visit our room — led to us excitedly discussing how we could translate the pleasure of interconnected puzzles into a book, while still restricting progression in the same way as a physical lock does.

This is that book. It is both a story that leads you from room to room, and a puzzle challenge in which you must uncover the correct way of solving the puzzles. The narrative in this book — that of the Wexell Corporation — can also be found in the real-life Deadlocked Rooms.

It has been an honour and a pleasure to be given the chance to create something so different and, without the incredible team behind it, it would never have ended up as something I can take such pride in. Thanks to everyone that assisted from listening to my crazy ideas to letting me run unfinished puzzles ideas past them. I hope that you all enjoy the experience you're about to go through.

The author, JAMES HAMER-MORTON, is the co-owner of Deadlocked Escape Rooms and Thinking Outside The Box Escape Rooms, and acts as a consultant for the Escape Room industry. When he is not designing and playing them, he spends his time acting; known for films such as *My Bloody Banjo* and *The Fitzroy*.

WELCOME TO
THE WEXELL CONSPIRACY

`ADAM PARKINSON.` Only it didn't really look like Adam Parkinson any more. More like "Adam Par...son". The name label on my small assigned postbox on the ground floor of my apartment complex had been worn down through years of gripping it in the same place every day. Now that I thought of it, the fact that it had lasted over four years was quite surprising considering I had no plastic cover on my name label, unlike all of the others in the building. The way that the words were wrong – yet still spelled a believable name – had started to intrigue me.

ADAM PARKINSON

I was convinced that one of my neighbours had swiped the covering soon after I had moved in, to cover one of their own immaculate names. But I couldn't be sure, and it was hardly the most important aspect of moving in to a new building. My girlfriend, Susan, had left me, and I was lucky to have found a place at all, let alone one so conveniently placed for my work as a junior editor at the *Evening Post*.

I was a reporter, of sorts... reporting on such exciting topics as stock markets shifting in the wake of an interview with a high-powered CEO, or the depressingly real statistical analyses of CO2 levels foreshadowing our inevitable doom. I still used a pseudonym — as if anyone would care what my name was — because I wanted to retain some kind of privacy if my career blossomed as I hoped it someday would. My mother's maiden name was my journalistic surname, serving to protect me from anti-climate change activists (an oxymoron if ever I heard one), but unfortunately also accidentally giving away the classic security password answer should any bank need it.

EVENIN

No.198

Scientist Breaks Neuron Field Interference Limit

By Adam Davies

If you share more than a passing interest in the field of Neuroscience, use yesterday's events to catch up on recent findings. A scientist named Professor Bradley Samwell has single-handedly, like a hot knife through butter, cut straight through the scientific community's repeated failed attempts to break the previously impenetrable NFI Limit. Before proceeding, any way you slice it, I have absolutely no idea what the NFI Limit is. My understanding is limited to Wexell, Samwell's current employer's, press release. My head is spinning.

Professor Samwell explains, "the Neuron Field regulates the mind and if you break the NFI Limit, you unlock an influence over minds. Weep or laugh, theoretically we could control emotions, implant suggestions. Naturally, it's beside the point until technology catches up. The mind is fascinating. To me, how it works naturally is more interesting than how it works when being influenced. Many are eager to explore such an influence, but I'm convinced it is a very dangerous door to open and you're dead wrong if you think we should."

My key had never worked on my postbox, so I had put a cheap numerical padlock on the lock to give myself some security. But perhaps it was too cheap, or I should have gone for a four-digit combination lock rather than the three-digit one that happened to be the cheapest in my local supermarket, because the code wasn't working for me now.

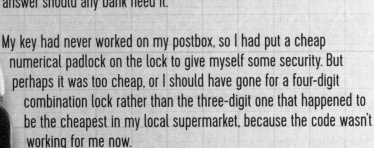

562 — THE FINAL THREE DIGITS OF MY PHONE NUMBER.

I wasn't that familiar with the internal workings of a padlock, but I was pretty sure that the code couldn't just spontaneously change. Had I accidentally changed it when I last locked it, or was someone else in my building playing a practical joke on me?

I looked over at the names of my neighbours on their postboxes. Mrs Eversham wouldn't have the knowhow to change a padlock, and Ms Nixon, although she sported a healthy sense of humour, wouldn't be inclined to this level of mischief. IT HAD TO BE MY DOWNSTAIRS NEIGHBOUR AND FRIEND, HENRY FIELDING.

EVENING POST

HENRY
FIELDING

I was obviously tired — I should have come to this conclusion straight away. Henry's mind worked a little differently to everyone else I knew. He used to work for the *Post* too; in fact he had let me know about the empty flat in his building when I was reeling from my break-up, and helped me move in. Eventually he left the paper because of "creative differences". Basically, he was always looking for a grand conspiracy to report on, and often filled his spots with conjecture and outrageous theories rather than any actual news. He became a freelancer, and kept up his unique way of thinking. He'd been on at me about a supposedly top-secret Roman ruin last week. His willingness to involve others in his craziness led to him sometimes setting strange but harmless challenges.

THIS WAS CLEARLY ONE OF THEM.

I looked back at the postboxes, and noticed something was different and not how it should be. I thought over how everything had looked this morning and realized there were some clear differences. AFTER FIVE MINUTES, I knew what he had changed the three-digit code on my padlock to. When I was sure that I had found it, I opened the postbox.

WELCOME TO
THE WEXELL CONSPIRACY

ADAM PARKINSON

AL SON EVERSHAM

L SA NI ON

ANIL KHAN

OLI ER W LSON

HENRY F ELD NG

How could I have missed the lock?

CHAPTER ONE:
ADAM'S APARTMENT

...the new combination to my postbox lock. What possible reason could Henry have for changing the code?

This wasn't the first time he had left me small inconsequential puzzles to test me, just as a bit of fun. A Sudoku here, a magic square there... but to lock me away from my own post seemed extreme. I looked inside the box and found a sheet of paper with what looked like schematics drawn on it. There was a scissors icon in the corner and I realised that I was expected to cut the paper. WHAT IF I MADE A MISTAKE? I thought about whether I wanted to risk ruining something that could potentially be important to me, given that Henry had locked it up, but figured that if it had a scissors icon on it then it was designed for me to cut out. However, if I had had more time to prepare, perhaps I COULD HAVE PHOTOCOPIED THE PAGE BEFORE TEARING INTO IT WITH A CUTTING IMPLEMENT.

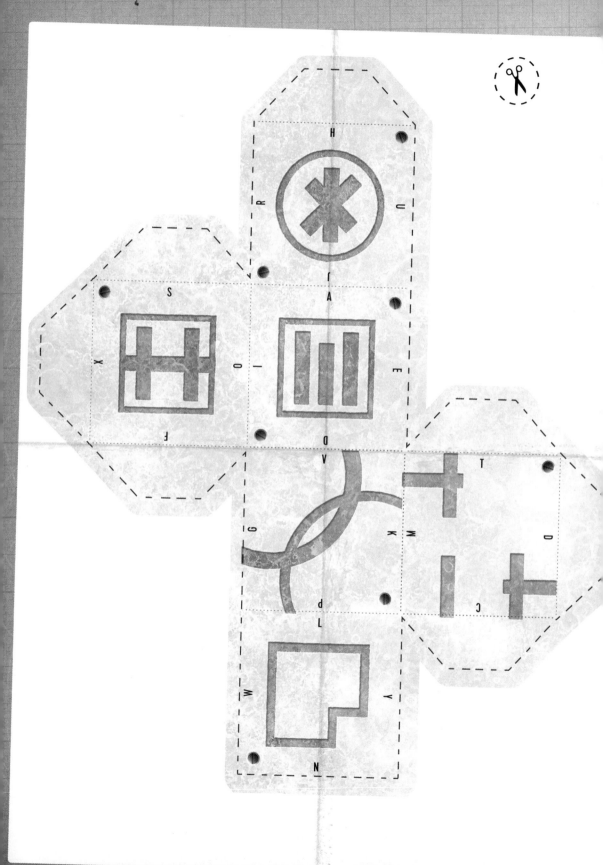

Underneath the paper was the item itself, made out of metal with engraved letters on each side. I folded the paper into my pocket; `AT LEAST I COULD REPLICATE THE ITEM IF I MISPLACED IT,` and it had to be important for him to leave it here for me to find.

Gripping the metal cube, I climbed the stairs to my apartment. Had Henry done anything else? I couldn't help but look at everything with fresh eyes. `EACH STEP COULD REVEAL A CANVAS FOR SOME NEW INFORMATION.` The walls looked as shabby as before and nothing seemed particularly different. Maybe the postboxes were all he had changed? Yet the ambiguous reasoning behind his actions concerned me. There was probably more. Face to face with my front door, I saw a Post-it note behind the handle.

He had wanted to ensure I had seen his puzzle before I went into my flat.

Dont
forget your
Mail

I was relieved to find that my key still worked; he hadn't broken in and changed the locks. But on opening the door I realised that he had definitely broken in. My living room wasn't as I had left it. The lock wasn't damaged, and I always leave the windows locked, so it had to have been someone that I had left a key with for emergencies. Henry had been into my flat.

BUT WHY? I had told him time and time again to respect my privacy, but he always put what he called his "work of great importance" ahead of my wishes. I closed the door behind me, noticing too late a small device attached to the wall next to it. As the handle slipped from my fingers and the door slotted into place, the device sprang to life, shooting a metal bar in front of the handle that stopped me pulling the door open again. The device was metallic and strange; its innards were masked from me, but I could see how I would have to remove it. A SERIES OF BUTTONS, LIKE A NORMAL NUMERICAL PAD BUT WITH IMAGES OF ANIMALS INSTEAD OF NUMBERS, WAS ATTACHED.

A sheep, a cat, a snake.

WERE THEY RELATED? HOW WAS IT POWERED? I realised something had been a bit funny when I walked into my flat earlier: a thick cable had been sticking out of the wall on the left side of the door. I didn't notice it immediately, but it shouldn't have been there.

I had to find the code. I was now trapped in my own apartment! A small *LED* number panel on the lock instantly jumped to 60:00 and began ticking down, second by second. I HAD AN HOUR TO ESCAPE before, I assumed, the lock would close forever. I looked up at the doorframe and realised that I couldn't unscrew the hinges or release the door in any other way other than removing this device. Naturally if things got desperate I could probably find something with which I could break the door down, but was that really wise? This was probably some harmless game, and I didn't want to suffer the expense of replacing my front door. I could always reconsider if my time ran out.

My next thought was to wonder if this was really Henry. This seemed far more extreme than anything he had done to me before, and yet who else did I know that would set up something so elaborate without stealing anything of note? My television was still in place. My laptop, an easy target for thieves, lay squarely on my table. I had a place for everything in my apartment (if I ever saw a photo frame slightly off centre, I would have to correct it, even if I was in a rush), and I couldn't see anything obviously out of place at first glance. But perhaps with further exploration, I would be able spot what else what Henry had changed. I looked around, hunting for clues. My typewriter lay on a side table near the soft leather sofa. It was slightly at an angle – Henry had moved it. Why did I have a typewriter? Of course, the modern age requires digital work, especially for a journalist like me, so I guess this was more of a status symbol than a practical object. A bit like a musician who owns guitars played by rock legends with no intention to play them. The only difference being that my typewriter wasn't owned by any Pulitzer Prize-winning writers or great novelists. It was just old and beautiful, and I couldn't resist picking it up from the antique store in which I had found it.

Without thinking, I straightened it, forgetting that I could be destroying a potential clue. But perhaps there was something more unusual than the angle I had found it at that I should have noticed straight away... Next to it was an open "*PUB QUIZ*" book that I had been given as a birthday present last year. This was one of those presents that you imagine will be fun to use to host a quiz when a group of friends come over, but for some reason you never do it. Truth be told, I hadn't even looked at the book, which made it even more strange that the book was open and in plain sight.

ROUND 4

Round 4 is the letter-clue round. You will be given 10 statements or questions and the starting letter of the answers you are looking for. Good luck!

1) Which **"T"** is a traditional place to stop for drinks?

2) This **"N"** is something your friends call you instead of your name.

3) This **"C"** is the quality of being mutable.

4) He's so stubborn, he's practically a living example of **"O"**.

5) Which **"H"** indicates that something is difficult, or tough to cut?

6) This **"M"** is another way of saying I have blended.

7) Which **"C"** means "possible to cure"?

8) These **"D"** believe in government by the people.

9) If you're **"L"**, you're not there on time.

10) What **"F"** links classical elements to an emergency service?

I wouldn't necessarily call myself obsessive compulsive; the name label on my postbox didn't irritate me quite enough to bother changing it myself, despite the odd passive aggressive comment to my landlord about it. But I like my things in the right place. That's why my eyes were drawn next to the newspaper I have delivered every morning. I had brought it inside and carefully laid it on my sofa after perusing it over breakfast. Henry had left it open; at the puzzles page, fittingly.

I normally take a look at the crossword after work, so the fact that he had started filling in some of the answers was both surprising and frustrating. Why would he spend the time to solve so much of a crossword when he was setting my apartment up for this strange trap? It had to be important somehow. Upon closer inspection, I realised that the words he had used weren't English. 12 DOWN WAS FILLED IN AS IGNIS. In fact, all of the words were written in Latin, and the questions section of the page had been ripped off. I didn't know enough Latin to understand all of the words, but knew that a quick internet search would probably assist.

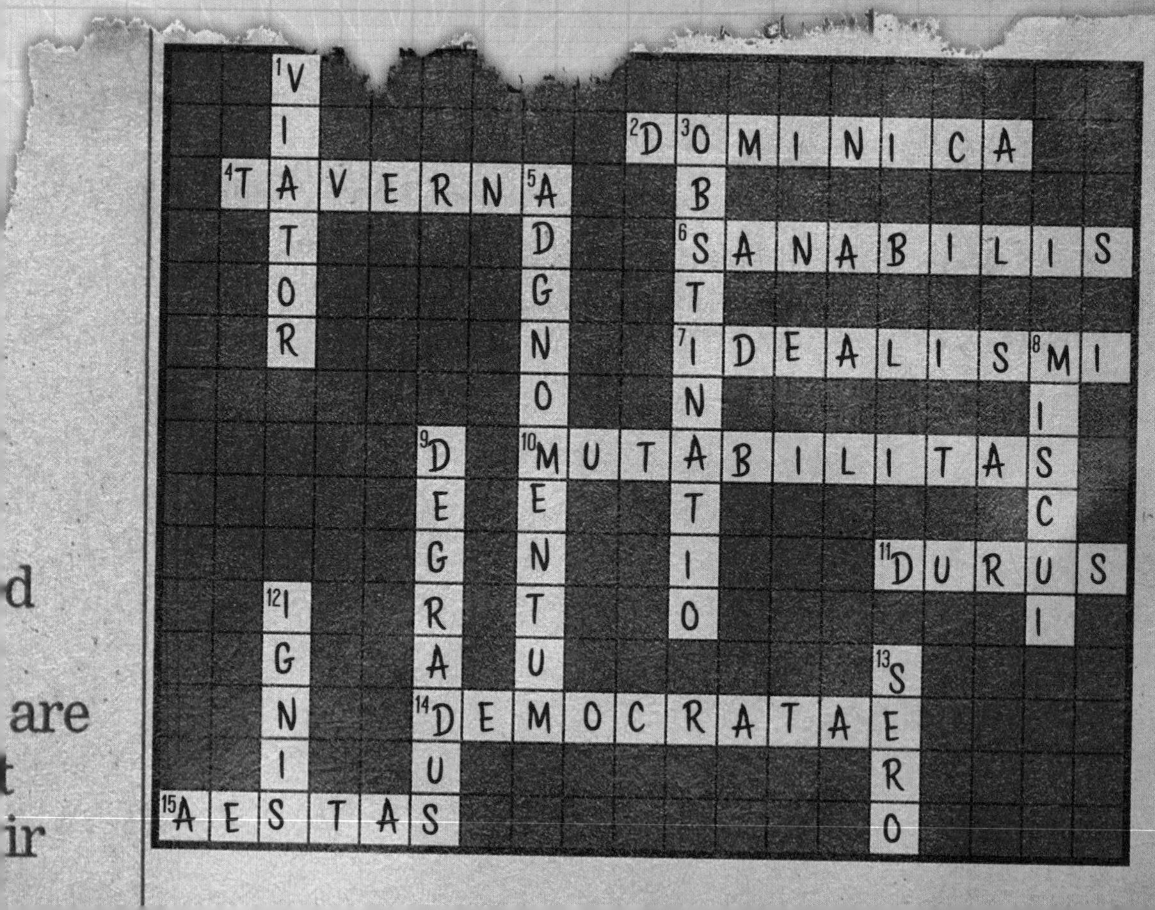

d

are

t

ir

I looked around a little more and discovered a photo sitting on my table. It had been defaced, and that frustrated me more than the installation of a locking system on my door that I had no way of opening. The words PHOTOS WITHOUT THEM had been written on the top of it.

Photos without them

WHAT COULD IT MEAN? I looked closer; it was a group of my friends on a bachelor party. Not mine, I might add. I was well and truly single, perhaps in no small way because of the kinds of friends I kept. Friends that would apparently use my apartment for an elaborate treasure hunt rather than popping over for a G&T and a game of cards!

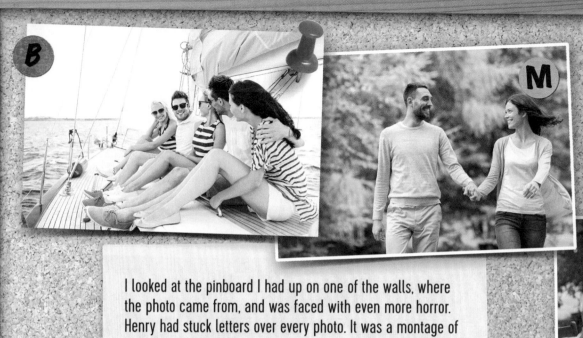

I looked at the pinboard I had up on one of the walls, where the photo came from, and was faced with even more horror. Henry had stuck letters over every photo. It was a montage of my life; every significant moment, every significant person... and now far too many stickers that looked like they wouldn't come off without leaving a mark.

Don't get me wrong, many of these photos were taken digitally and could be replicated. The rest I had scanned onto my laptop. But the thought of the time, effort and, of course, money that would be involved to fix the mess that Henry had caused was leaving me very unsettled.

I still felt I needed proof that this was Henry. Of course, I didn't know anyone else that would act like a serial killer, taunting his pursuers with puzzles designed to give away his secrets, just for fun, but I still... What was that? How could I not have seen it before? Pinned to the back of my door was a letter which had been written to explain things a little.

Dear Adam,

This letter is not written to explain everything that has been changed in your room. I hope that, in time, you will understand the purpose of what I have set up here, and understand why I have done what I have done. I was reading one of your previous articles, about a scientist who worked for the Wexell Corporation, whom I was investigating at the time. It didn't really seem like something you had written. Was your article doctored somehow, perhaps by "them"? I realised that you may have a stake in finding the truth about them, but frankly I can't risk anyone else finding the information I have uncovered. It could put me, and them, in danger. That said, I'm doing this now because I have a feeling that I have come to their attention, and this may be my last chance to tell someone. I believe in you, Adam, and I believe that you can get to the bottom of what may be the greatest conspiracy in modern times. Yes, I may be a slave to hyperbole, but I wouldn't be doing this if I didn't think it was real. Hopefully, you will escape the room within the hour and find my apologetic face on the other side of the door. If you do not, then you will know why I am not there - the Wexell Corporation - and, I pray, believe me enough to pursue the thread that has led me into the trouble I believe I am in. Perhaps you will be glad that I have typed this letter after all.

E och in hnvts socs rnv xnvlh zeih soep pmaseni nz smjs. Xmll hnim, Chcu. Som anhm sn mpacbm aci tm znvih vpeiy som bonsnp, somi som esmu E lmzs rnv ei som bnps tnj, somi som aknppxnkh uepscdmp. Bvpo sompm sokmm tvssnip ei soep nkhmk cih rnv xell mpacbm.

If you do not succeed in time, the lock will open and you will be able to leave, but you won't have what it takes to save me. I don't want you to put yourself in danger without being sure that you can achieve what I need you to achieve. Escaping the room in time will prove it.

Good luck, and my apologies for bringing you into this.

Henry Fielding

I stood back, more stunned at the revelation that Henry was behind this than I should have been, having already assumed this was his doing. I had an objective; TRANSLATE THE LETTER, AND FIGURE OUT WHAT BUTTON COMBINATION WOULD LET ME OUT OF MY APARTMENT. I took one final look around for anything unusual and something caught my eye, in what I optimistically call my trophy cabinet.

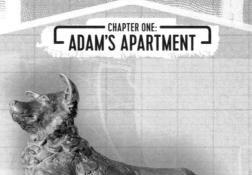

MOST PROMISING NEWCOMER

It was a display case for all of my most precious possessions. All of them. Currently the actual value of its contents was probably less than that of my refrigerator, but that didn't stop me having some pride in it. I had won an award, early in my career, from a lesser known journalistic entity for "MOST PROMISING NEWCOMER", which essentially just meant that I had impressed someone by being new to the world of journalism. It was an expensive-looking (if not feeling) golden statuette in the shape of a sheepdog. I guess the act of "sniffing out" a lead was as tenuous a link as was needed for the Academy of Journalistic Excellence.

In reality, I had written an article on the basis of my English professor's suggestion that "something was going on with the local water company". An article of conjecture, and an interview with someone that thought I was more experienced than I was, happened to draw attention to the fluoride levels of the local supply, and suddenly I was an accidental hero. SHAUN THE SHEEPDOG was the highlight of my career according to my extended family, one of whom, my nephew Miles, had grown strangely attached to the golden mutt.

I had promised him that he could have the award as soon as I'd won one better, and from then on, every birthday and Christmas, he would give me a new statue that he had hand-crafted from papier mache or clay from his school's art department. My cabinet was now full of them. There was Joe the sheep — someone for Shaun to chase around — Alf the dodo — because I once joked that my career was as dead as one — and so many others that it risked turning my apartment into a zoo. I was pleased to see that everything was still in place as the sentimental value of a vacuum formed snake couldn't be underestimated, but what was on the bottom platform clearly reminded me of Henry's insane game.

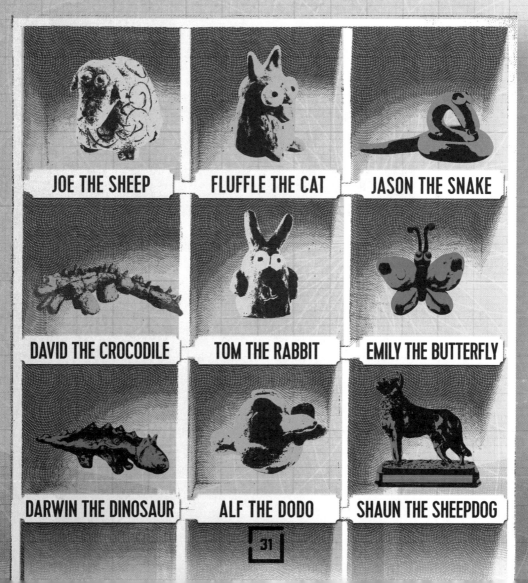

JOE THE SHEEP

FLUFFLE THE CAT

JASON THE SNAKE

DAVID THE CROCODILE

TOM THE RABBIT

EMILY THE BUTTERFLY

DARWIN THE DINOSAUR

ALF THE DODO

SHAUN THE SHEEPDOG

A single piece of card lay on the shelf, with three rectangles on it and arrows pointing to an edge on each rectangle. They looked familiar. After a few seconds, I realised where I had seen them before; they were images of the sides of the cube that Henry had left me in my post box. That had to be related to this, and be some part of his master plan.

Taking a step back and looking over the entire room, I started to get a picture of how everything fit together. I needed to find three animals that were on the keypad to let me out of my apartment. Once I was sure that I'd found what I needed `I COULD PROCEED,` but first I needed to translate that section of Henry's letter.

For difficult hints turn to page 190
For medium hints turn to page 193
For easy hints turn to page 198
For solutions turn to page 206

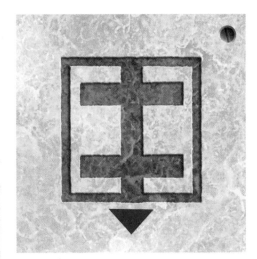

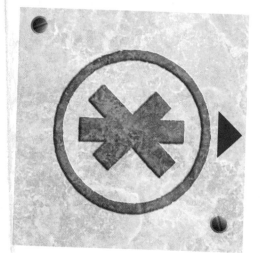

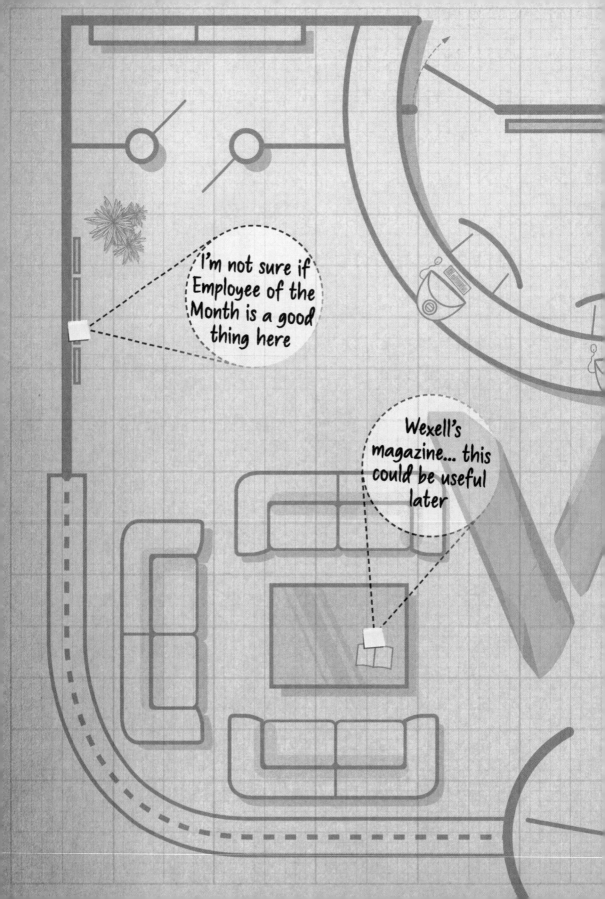

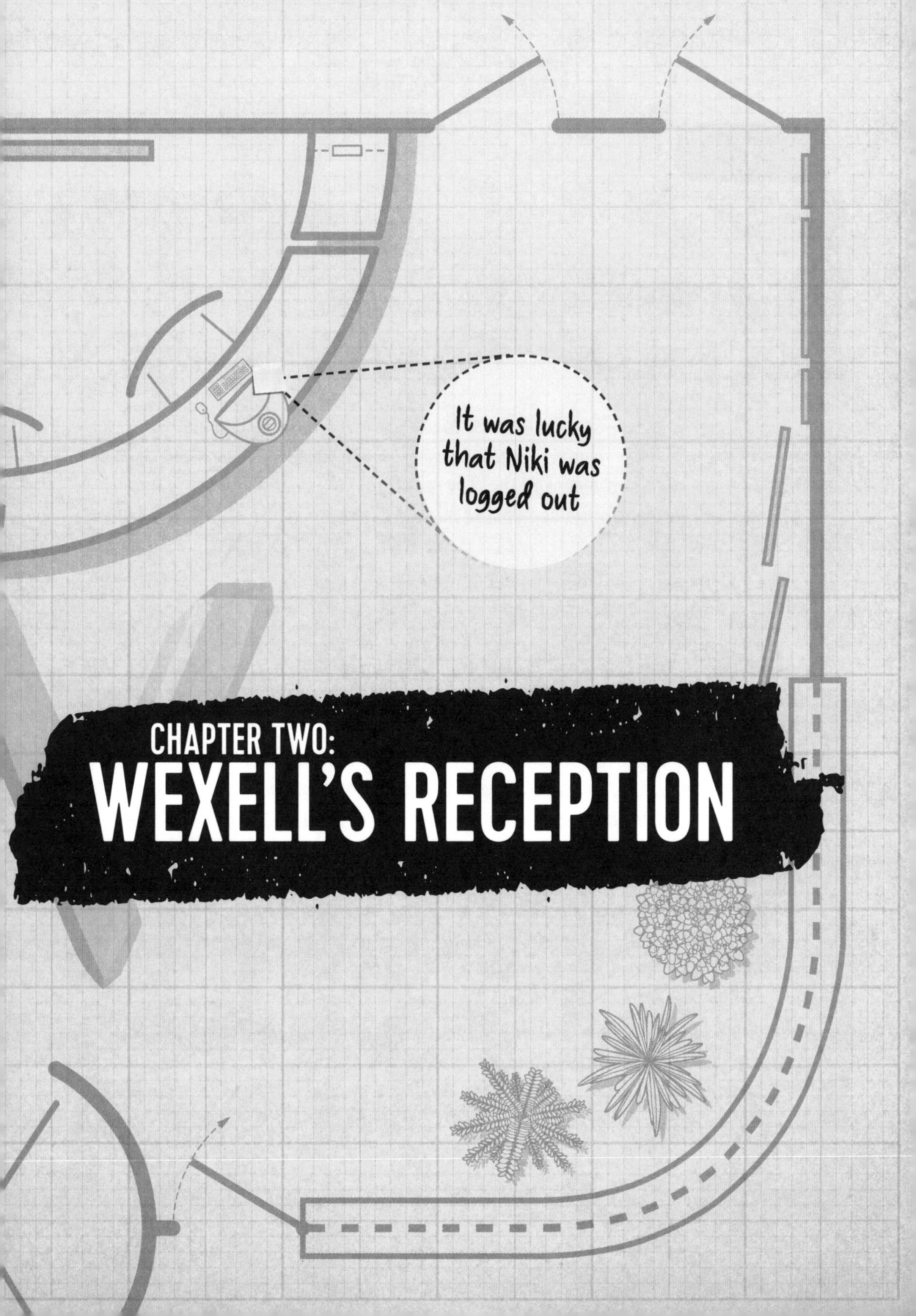

It was lucky that Niki was logged out

CHAPTER TWO:
WEXELL'S RECEPTION

I pushed the keys in the order that I had figured out from the letter, the crossword, the trophies and the photos.

Butterfly, Sheep, Crocodile.

The panel let out a double beep and the metal bar retracted back into the rest of the device. I breathed a sigh of relief, but the silence was swiftly broken by Henry's voice emanating from the door.

"Congratulations, Adam, you've figured it out in time."
"Henry?" I replied, sensing something was different about his voice.
"This is a pre-recorded message that I have left for you, playing from the item I attached to your doorframe, for which I must apologise."

I looked down, recognised the source of the sound and couldn't help but feel stupid for talking to it. The voice continued:

"By completing my challenge in time, you have unlocked this recording which will hopefully explain what I couldn't be sure that you would have the knowledge and intelligence to handle."
"Charming." I quipped, forgetting once more that Henry wasn't actually there.
"I have made a rather interesting discovery about an international organisation known as the Wexell Corporation. I use the term organisation, because although they are in business to make money, they seem to have a long and varied history, transcending their current practises. Indeed I started to believe that they had some kind of grand purpose beyond their shareholders. Think of them like 'The Illuminati', but real."
Henry was the last person I would expect to say that. A conspiracy theorist that disputed the existence of the Illuminati?

"The more I looked into Wexell, the more I realised that they had more secrecy than standard business practises; pouring billions into research and development that seemingly had no results, yet keeping their investors happy. How does that

make any sense? Indeed, it was one of your articles that turned me onto them. A feature on a researcher who worked for them, who disappeared shortly after you had written about him."

I remembered the article, but nothing about the subject's disappearance. He was someone I had known for quite some time, and had made a few concessions for, especially in this article, because he seemed desperate. I took out my phone and called his number, while listening to the rest of Henry's speech. If I got an answer, it would prove him wrong.

"I've never lied to you, Adam. I've never exaggerated any proof I have found, especially not to you. Please trust me on this."

My phone chirped up with `"THIS NUMBER HAS NOT BEEN RECOGNISED. PLEASE TRY AGAIN."` Could this be real?

"It's as simple as this. I've taken the time to set all this up. All I'm going to do is go to my flat, wait for you to come home and then wait outside your flat. If you open your front door and I'm standing there, then you know everything is fine, but if I'm not, I need you to promise me you will find me. If they have taken me, and you have unlocked this recording, you're the only person I trust to be able to free me and uncover the truth behind Wexell. Promise me, Adam."

There was a pause. I knew the recording couldn't hear me, but I couldn't help but feel like responding.
"I can't hear you, Adam. Say that you promise."
Maybe he could hear, or there was some kind of elaborate voice recognition built into the box. *"I promise!"*
"This is a recording, but I'll assume you've just promised me. Now open the door, and I hope that for both of our sakes, you see my smiling face on the other side."

I clenched the door handle. If Henry wasn't there, I didn't know what I'd do. I swung it open. Henry wasn't there. `THE WEXELL CORPORATION HAD TAKEN HIM.`

Unsurprisingly, public transport had good links to one of the largest "organisations" in the world. I strode up to the entrance, not really sure what I was doing or what my plan was. All I had was my reporter's notebook, which I took with me everywhere. At least it was the perfect time for it; 7pm. There would only be a skeleton crew on site, but if Henry had been taken to the main London headquarters, he would be inside somewhere. I couldn't see any sign of security other than a few CCTV cameras dotted around the ceiling. They were those circular pods that hid exactly where they were looking. Or perhaps they were looking at everything. A lady in a Wexell-branded shirt walked past me.

The receptionist on the front desk called out, *"Night, Niki!"* to the lady as she left.
"Good night." She replied.
"Can I help you, sir?"

The receptionist had shifted her attention to me. I decided to wait until I got closer before talking back, though as I awkwardly semi-jogged over to the front desk, I realised that the room was a lot bigger than I had expected. A cursory look around let me spot a series of "Employee of the Month" photos. Everyone looked far too happy for this to be a legitimate award. I thought they looked more like stock photos.

JANUARY

Joined Wexell: September 13th, 2013
"Work towards your dreams and you'll never be fishing for the next promotion or the next car."

Wexell
EMPLOYEE OF THE MONTH 2018

FEBRUARY

Joined Wexell: January 20th, 2015
"Building a better future takes time and effort, but take a step back or you'll not see the forest for the trees."

MARCH

Joined Wexell: February 27th, 2012
"I dedicate this award to my pet cat and pet bird whom my pet cat chases all around the house."

APRIL

Joined Wexell: December 28th, 2015
"People are more than the sum of their achievements. That said, I like this one."

MAY

Joined Wexell: August 18th, 2005
"Why do I need to give you a quote for some meaningless award? Do I get a pay rise?"

JUNE

Joined Wexell: November 13th, 2007
"The ABCs of a great working environment are A = People, B = Buildings, C = Trees and probably last, Z = Cars"

JULY

Joined Wexell: March 12th, 2016
"It's important to have rooms to grow within. Otherwise how can you afford the latest car?"

AUGUST

Joined Wexell:October 30th, 2007
"Personally, I've carried on with my life treemendously well while at Wexell."

SEPTEMBER

Joined Wexell: February 3rd, 2012
"Out of all the people in the world, my girlfriend is my favourite. She pushed me to achieve here rather than just look out of the window dreaming."

OCTOBER

Joined Wexell: July 4th, 2011
"Watching the people milling around under the trees outside gives me the serenity to get my work done. Definitely prioritise having windows."

I finally reached the desk, and stupidly thought it would be endearing to fake being out of breath. The receptionist kept smiling, though I could tell it was tinted with a superior air of disgust, like I had just walked in off the street and really shouldn't be there. Which was accurate, I suppose.

Her name tag said 'Diane Llewellyn', and that was all I had to go on to try to get further into the building.

"Hello, Diane is it?"

"Yes. That's why it says Diane on my name badge."

"Of course."

"So. Can I help you?"

"I have an appointment."

"At this time of day?"

"Well, not an official appointment. More like I'm meeting a friend. Do you mind if I just... wait here, until she comes down?"

I had thought this through on the tube. Suggesting I knew someone in the company that was female would allow me to get away with saying an unrecognised surname and blame it on a married or maiden name much more easily if I said the wrong name.

"Look, I've been working here since 2010, and I greet every person coming into this building and I've never seen you before in my life."

"Well, that's probably because I've never been here before. My friend is working late, and we're going out. It was either meet her here or wait outside, and it's getting cold."

"Fine. By all means take a seat."

"Thank you." I joined her in a forced smile. "I might just have a look if I can spot her on your walls if that's okay."

"Knock yourself out." She conceded.

I was in. Not exactly in as far as I needed to be, but I had free roam of the reception area and could take my time. I noticed a large display, no doubt intended to enthuse employees and investors about the progress of the company and its development. Apparently, Wexell was EXPANDING TO A HUGE CAMPUS IN HAMPSHIRE. A large map of a building, with an "artist's impression" of what it would look like when it was finished, dwarfed the rest of the room. Buzzwords like "renewable energy" and "self-powered" glowed ominously on the display. It all looked a bit ridiculous. They had even included birds and cats in the poster... and was that a police car?

The Wexell Corporation is **BUILDING** a new home for our **EUROPEAN OPERATIONS** in the heart of Hampshire, England. Our **MODERN OFFICES**, nicknamed **"THE CENTRE"**, will be entirely **SELF-POWERED** using **RENEWABLE ENERGY** with a few secure areas for our more **IMPORTANT RESEARCH** projects.

THE CENTRE – THE FUTURE OF WORKSPACES
www.wexellcorp.com

I turned around and came face to face with a large bald man in a suit and an earpiece. He had to be security.

"What are you doing in here at this time of night?"
"Meeting someone. I'll be out of your hair soon."

I PRAYED HE HADN'T TAKEN
OFFENCE TO MY CHOICE OF WORDS.

"You'd better be," he insisted, *"if I see you after my rounds, you'll regret it."*
"Out of interest, how long are your rounds?"
"It takes me about 60 minutes to get around the whole building, if you really want to know."

I glanced down at my watch, noting the time limit now in place. I had an hour to figure out some way of getting further into the building. I looked around, flummoxed. To even get through the door to the elevators I needed to get past an ID card scanner. I watched the bald man walk through, scan his ID, and the entire door lit up in a green glow. But he didn't just walk through. Looking back over his shoulder, he reached over to a keypad and tapped in 5 digits. Was that his own code, or a code for the entire building? Just getting out of the reception area was proving to be much trickier than anticipated, let alone finding Henry. I needed to look over the entire area and see if there was anything that could help me.

STOPWATCH

60:00

CHAPTER TWO:
WEXELL'S RECEPTION

Walking slowly across the reception area, something caught my eye. A Wexell ID card lay on the floor, leant up against the side of the sleek sofa in what was intended to be the waiting area. I palmed it, picked up the company magazine on the table and started thumbing through it innocently. A nod and a smile over to the receptionist, and I knew I had gotten away with it. I turned my hand slowly to reveal the card.

Wexell employee Kieran Frost. ID number 0024003. A green bar sliced through the bottom of the card, which also revealed his job title was "Designer". Designer of what? His hardly flattering photo and a barcode completed the card. I flipped it over again; nothing on the back, but I figured that it would pay to be thorough. Now I had his ID card, perhaps I could use it to get past the scanner. But the receptionist knew too much of my presence here. She knew that I didn't work here, and that I certainly wouldn't have an ID card to let me in. I had to get rid of her somehow. WHILE I WAITED TO COME UP WITH A PLAN, I thumbed through a few pages of the WEXELL MAGAZINE while she threw her attention at something she was writing behind the desk.

The magazine gave me an insight into the inner workings of Wexell, no doubt filtered through the best PR company, but nothing else instantly stood out. I felt obligated to stand up and look around the room more intently, but feared the receptionist's eyes would be watching me. As if by magic, she picked up her phone, laughed and trotted off towards what I assumed was the bathroom. This was my chance. I launched myself to my feet as soon as she was out of range, and tried the ID card on the security station. It turned green. THE CARD WAS VALID. I just needed his security code and I could get further into the building.

WEXELL Employee
ID #0024003
DESIGNER
Kieran
FROST

A WORD FROM OUR CEO

It is a pleasure to preface our monthly newsletter and this, the 34th edition, marks a very special time for me. In many ways, this year is an important anniversary of my own involvement in the Wexell Corporation. When I began, I was merely working in research, like many of you, and somehow now find myself running one of the world's leading companies.

Some people question our ethics. Some people question our methods. Everybody questions how we are able to achieve what we achieve, and I can only thank all of you for your dedication to our tasks, purposes and methodology which allows us all to soar. Thank you.

LEARNING WITH WEXIE!

Every month, our friendly robotic sidekick Wexie gives us some unusual knowledge to broaden our horizons with. This month, it's all about exotic pet fish. When designing an aquarium it is important to know how different fish interact with each other so that your tank can exist in a state of equilibrium.

The Black Toad will remain in the aquarium if there are less than 18 animals in the habitat, excluding itself. If it chooses to jump out, it will take all of the green bamboo – its home – that it can find with it, as a basis for a future home. Unfortunately it will not survive in a non-contained environment. The toad will eat any fish that has a red home unless a shrimp is also present.

The Pink Shrimp has a symbiotic relationship with the Black Toad, protected by it while removing parasites from it. Should there not be a Toad present, the Shrimp hides underneath a brown log, its preference for its home. It wedges itself underneath it tightly, so that the slightest movement of the log will crush and kill it.

The Green Dogfish loves to eat any dead animals unfortunate enough to pass away inside the aquarium, but will not directly attack any others. It will eat animals in the order of their demise and can manage two distinct fish before it stops feeding. If it eats a Ghostfish, it will head into the largest contained

environment – a Castle – and wait there passively. Should it eat a Shrimp, it will be poisoned and sadly die almost immediately. Its home is a silver shell.

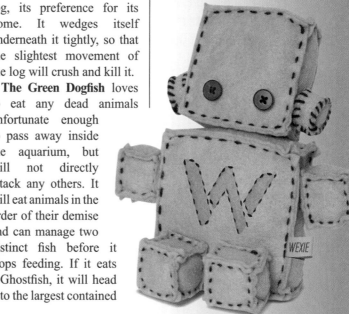

WEXIE

The White Ghostfish will immediately eat all Flattyfish in the area unless it feels secure by knowing that there is a red treasure chest, its home, somewhere in the vicinity, even if it cannot currently see it. If the Ghostfish witnesses a fish being poisoned, it will become distressed and scared and will bury itself in any mud at the base of the aquarium, which will cloud the entire environment, temporarily making the rest of the fish unable to see. If this happens, after about a minute, when the water clears, it will seek shelter anywhere blue and wait there until equilibrium is once again reached.

The Blue Doublefish always stays close to its home base, anywhere with the same colour as it, where it can be camouflaged. If it stops being able to see, it becomes aggressively defensive, retreating into its home, and killing anything either inside it or that enters its home that is not trying to eat it itself.

The Silver Skinnyfish only hunts Dollyfish, but only when it is the dominant fish in its environment numerically. If there are more Skinnyfish than the sum of the other animals put together, it is dominant. Its home is underneath the orange bridge. If it is left alone with a Bronzefish, it will eat it.

The Yellow Dollyfish hunts and kills all of its enemy, the Skinnyfish, but only when there are more Dollyfish than Skinnyfish in the habitat. If another fish tries to hide near its home, the cream stones, the Dollyfish will lash out and kill one Skinnyfish for every fish hiding there.

The Bronzefish eats all of the fern in the environment if it feels that its normal food, the bamboo, is no longer present. Once the fern is eaten, it will hide in its home, the black cave.

The Red Flattyfish hunts and eats any blue fish unless there are yellow fish in the aquarium. If there are no Dollyfish present, it will kill all Skinnyfish in the area. It considers any solid grey objects its home.

The Grey Catfish lives in the pink coral. If its food supply of fern is destroyed or eaten, it becomes violent and hunts around, disturbing and knocking over anything brown, to see if there is any fern nearby. It is a very social fish, and prefers living in greater numbers. If there are only three types of fish left alive, visible or not, then it will eat all of the Flattyfish, unless the third type is a Skinnyfish. However, if it feels like it is the last type of animal alive, because it cannot see any others, it will become extremely scared and die of distress.

While I had some time, I thought I'd take the opportunity to check the reception desk, in case this was my one chance; if `I WAS GOING TO BREAK INTO THE BUILDING`, I might as well go all out. The standard fare of office equipment littered the area around the computer. Her journal was sitting in the open, and a picture of her and her partner was showing as her screensaver. `I COULDN'T RESIST TAKING A PEEK AT HER JOURNAL`.

Niki.Pelling

Rather than waiting for the rest of the journal to be completed, I thought I'd better move on. `SHE HAD DILIGENTLY LOGGED OUT OF HER COMPUTER`, but the mention of her password intrigued me. If I could figure out her username and her password I could access the machine. A company like this wouldn't give her the option of username – probably a combination of first name and surname – but I still needed to figure out the way the combination worked and, of course, her password. I looked around the room and it dawned on me that I had probably seen enough to be able to suss it all out. I double-checked the information, and when I was sure that `I HAD THE RECEPTIONIST'S USERNAME AND PASSWORD, I KNEW I COULD PROCEED.`

11th November - Boss gave me a pay rise today. Said she'd never seen a worker take no sick days in the best part of a decade. I've seen too many people fired from Wexell for much less than that, and it is not like rent is getting any cheaper in London. I need the money. I would rather power through than wallow in self-pity. I have always been different to my friends like that. They would rather go out on Friday/Saturday night so that they can recover on the weekend. I would rather go out any other day and be paid to recover at work. Then at least I don't waste one of my days off.

Mandatory password change today. It seems like there is a new threat of cyber attacks every week, but I guess it is a good thing. BF would hate it, but I have changed my password to the first day I met him. It's even 15 digits! Actually, knowing him, it would probably give him some pride. Ironic really considering how lax he has been with his own security. He even tried to tell me his security code earlier, and I am sure someone must be monitoring his email; he's going to get fired.

Should really be going home now, but overtime is worth it, especially when no-one comes in after standard hours and security is floating around doing the real work.

Scratch that, guess I am babysitting some guy that's hanging around in the lobby waiting for some bimbo who is probably sleeping with her boss...

I entered the receptionist's username as Diane.Llewellyn and password as 3rdFebruary2012 and hit enter. Invalid password. I was so sure that I had it. Of course! Wexell is an American company. All of their dates would be written with the month first, then the day, then the year. I tried "February3rd2012" and with a tap of the enter key, the machine sprang to life.

A messy desktop presented itself to me, with files and folders relating to what I could only describe as extra-curricular activities. I couldn't find anything directly related to Wexell or the business of running a reception desk. Rather, all I could see was pictures of cats, AMATEURISH POSTER DESIGNS FOR AN UPCOMING BAKE SALE and a notice clearly aimed at flatmates warning them to stay away from her food, no doubt posted on her refrigerator at home. She lost all semblance of respect by writing it in Comic Sans, unfortunately.

I noticed that her web browser was still open, and clicked through. I was presented with her email, and one stood out; a message from Kieran Frost, whose ID card I was brandishing. Diane and Kieran were clearly an item, which explained why he may have spent enough time in the reception to misplace his ID card. It was a long shot, but there might be a clue to his security code in there.

Was this the designer Kieran's handiwork? The poster had a Wexell logo at the bottom, with a website URL beneath it and a QR code. I had to assume it was a QR code link to the site. I took out my phone and scanned the code using a free QR code app and up popped my web browser. The site didn't load; was the server down? I double checked the address it had sent me to and realised there was a typo in the address. It said: www.wexellcount.com. What a silly mistake to make. Although, perhaps it wasn't a mistake. Looking back at the poster once more, I caught something that I

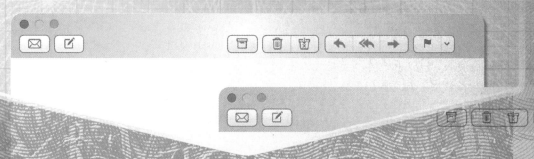

Kieran Frost

Re: Can you guess the code?

To: Diane Llewellyn

Hi babe,

You know how I'm always forgetting my card-code, and you're nice enough to remind me every morning? Well, management didn't really like it that much, so they made me change it last week. I thought it might be fun to alleviate your boredom by letting you figure it out, so I've been systematically hiding things in the design work I've been doing for reception to lead you to the code. If you're bored one day, see if you can figure it out. Just remember, my favourite colour is blue, then yellow, green and red.

P.S. I love you.

hadn't seen before. Some of the windows appeared to have been overlaid with a series of squares and a few of them had numbers in them. There was something vaguely familiar about them... After a minute or so, I realised what it was. IT LOOKED LIKE A SUDOKU THAT HAD BEEN DECONSTRUCTED AND SCATTERED AROUND. SOME OF THE BOXES LOOKED LIKE THEY HAD BEEN HIGHLIGHTED.

It took me some time to unravel the web of mystery that Kieran had set up, for Diane's benefit, but once I came across a 4-digit number that made sense, I KNEW I COULD PROCEED.

WEXELL Employee
ID #0024003
DESIGNER
Kieran FROST

I NERVOUSLY APPROACHED THE SECURITY STATION AND SWIPED THE ID CARD. I tapped in the numbers and paused. A green light flashed up, and I breathed a sigh of relief. Walking through, I remembered why I was here in the first place. Henry had been abducted by the Wexell Corporation and I needed to find and free him. I spotted the floor plan near to where I had swiped the ID card and saw "security - B3". That must be where he was locked up. I had to go down to the basement to find him. I called the elevator, stepped inside and hit the B3 button. It glowed ominously. I looked around to see quotes from the Wexell CEO, unnamed beyond his job title, promising that he was acting for the greater good, but the quotes were seemingly laced with veiled threats.

The elevator started descending. I was only going three floors down, but it seemed to take forever. Finally a high-pitched "bing" let me know that I had stopped. I glanced over at the control panel, out of habit rather than anything else, and I was faced with a sight I was really hoping I wouldn't see. "B2" was written on the LED display. I had stopped a floor early. Someone else had called the lift. The doors separated and I was stood in front of a familiar face. The bald man in a suit.

"I don't think you're meant to be here, are you mate?" He quipped.
I could only reply with an audible gulp.

He looked down at the button I had pushed that was still lit up.
"Good news though. You and me, we're going to the same place."
I had gone into Wexell to rescue my friend... and ended up in the same predicament as him

"ALWAYS DO YOUR BEST. THE ALTERNATIVE DOESN'T BEAR THINKING ABOUT."
— *Wexell's CEO*

"I ONLY REQUIRE THAT YOU WORK AS DILIGENTLY AS I AM FAIR IN REWARDING AND PUNISHING BEHAVIOUR."
— *Wexell's CEO*

"IF WE WANT TO SEE THE FUTURE, WE MUST FIRSTLY LOOK TO THE PAST."
— *Wexell's CEO*

"WE SHOULD ALL STRIVE TO LEARN FROM THE POTENTIAL FUTURES LYING AHEAD OF US WITHOUT EVEN HAVING EXPERIENCED THEM."
— *Wexell's CEO.*

For difficult hints turn to page 190
For medium hints turn to page 193
For easy hints turn to page 199
For solutions turn to page 207

CHAPTER THREE:
SECURITY OFFICE

Not the best chair I've ever sat in

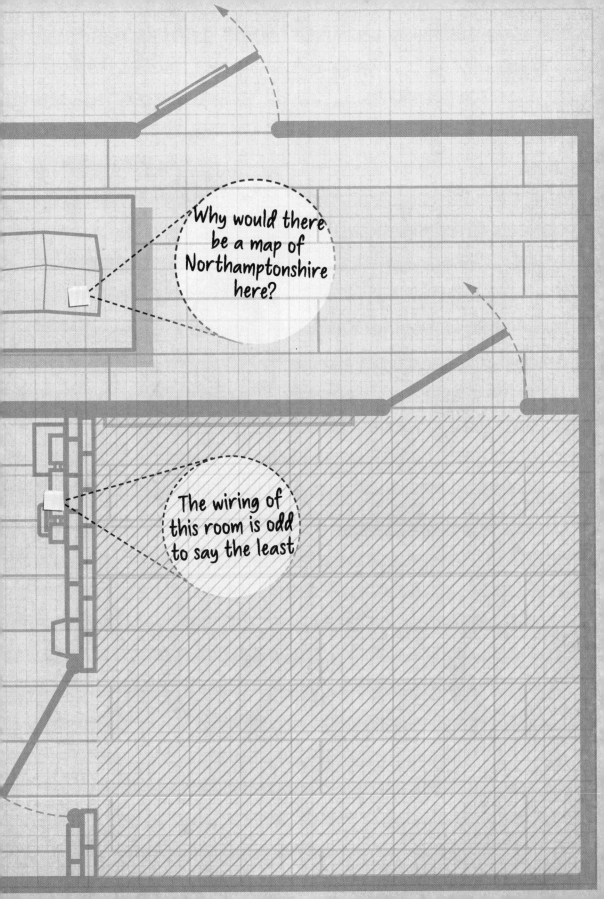

"Welcome to your home for the foreseeable future."

The bald man in a suit shoved me into a cold, dank room I could only describe as a cell. Some rescuer I was.

Two doors led out of the room; the first I had come in through, and as the man secretively punched in a code to exit, I listened intently. Five digits would let me out, but guessing them would take forever, not to mention possibly lock me in for good after a certain number of failed entries. The second door had a padlock on it — with a much more manageable 3-digit code — that held a heavy-looking sliding hatch closed. The door itself seemed to be magnetically sealed with a series of four dials that pointed to various letters; C I L V M D X.

Involuntarily, I turned them, as if I could trust my luck to randomly find the combination. I immediately regretted my actions when the third of the four dials snapped off in my hand. I tried to put it back on the cylindrical protrusion that held it initially, but didn't know which position to slot it into. Had I destroyed any chance of solving the code? Even if I knew it, I couldn't set the dial to the right letter. I twiddled the knob, which still turned, but clearly I had no idea what value it was set to.

Frustrated, and a little worried, I couldn't help but mutter my discomfort to myself. As if in response, I heard a shuffling from the room behind the second door. Suddenly I could hear something muffled from the other side. I couldn't quite make out the words, but it was definitely a human voice.

"I can't understand you!" I shouted back.
The mumbling stopped, soon to be replaced with clear banging on the door.

`BANG BANG BANG. BANG BANG BANG BANG.`
`BANG.`

Instantly, I realised that it was a deliberate pattern. 3, 4, 1. Was that the code to the padlock? My hands were shaking as I turned the dials on the combination padlock, ignoring the fact that the bangs had continued.

`BANG BANG BANG BANG.`
`BANG BANG BANG BANG BANG.`

The code didn't work. There was more to this than I had initially thought.

`BANG BANG BANG BANG BANG.`
`BANG BANG. BANG BANG.`

Then it stopped. It had to be important, but I had no clue why at this stage.

I TOOK A LONGER LOOK AROUND THE ROOM. It seemed sparsely decorated, but then what was I expecting from somewhere intended to store undesirables? I looked at myself in a wide mirror on the wall and wondered what I was doing.

It seemed I was the undesirable, breaking into a high-security building on the whim of my friend. But that didn't mean I didn't have a job to do. To the right of the mirror I spotted a series of electrical boxes with labels warning of danger and high voltages. Turning to look closer, I saw it was a seemingly random hotchpotch of wiring connecting boxes of different electrical specifications, makes and models.

Whoever was in charge of maintenance in this building either had a wide array of different needs or had been COBBLING TOGETHER PARTS IN A DESPERATE ATTEMPT to keep the power running. But why were they in this security office? Maybe the threat of danger was enough to avoid captives messing around with the boxes. I gave a couple of covers a quick tug to see if I could open them, but fortunately, for my own safety, none of them opened. Above them, on the dirty looking bricks, was a series of numbers written regularly on the bricks in a pattern. I noticed none of them were repeated, and something told me there was more to them than just random numbers.

ON THE WALL OPPOSITE THE MIRROR was a series of coloured lines that seemed nonsensical, with arrow points at one end of each line. They made shapes that could be patterns, or perhaps the semblance of letters, but nothing seemed legible immediately.

There was a metal chair sat next to a table and what looked like an old two-way radio system. A BUTTON UNDER A MICROPHONE WAS TOO TEMPTING FOR ME TO AVOID. I held it down, heard a comforting radio click and greeted whoever may have been on the other side.

"Hello?"

Nothing. Perhaps the machine wasn't connected to anything, or simply no-one was on the other side.

I spun around and noticed an arrow on the back of the chair. Lifting it up revealed a strange 5x5 grid with numbers and arrows. Did I have to fill that grid in?

Nothing else immediately stood out to me, and my mind rushed to make sense of the series of unusual factors surrounding me. Did I have enough information to figure out what the bangs meant, and whether or not they would lead me to opening one of the locks? I needed to be sure, and after 15 minutes I had put most of the elements in the room together. I had a 3-digit number and I KNEW I COULD PROCEED.

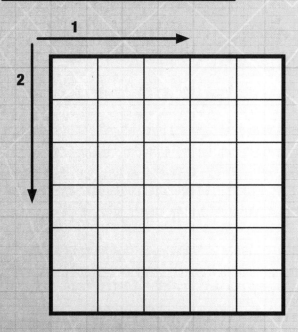

I tried "930" on the padlock, the voltage of the "Trix" model electrical box on the wall, and tugged on the metal casing. It smoothly released to my satisfaction, and I breathed a sigh of relief. Sliding the padlock from its hook, I pulled the metal cover aside and jumped as I saw, facing me, the eyes of my friend Henry Fielding.

"Henry?"
"Adam!"
"You were right... about Wexell. What are they doing to you?"
"Oh, you know. Stopping me from talking to anyone else. Asking me about my work. Convincing me that what they're doing is for the best... All of which just confirms to me that my investigation is of great importance! "
"And what are they doing?"
"I don't know yet. I just know that people have gone missing – prominent people in the company – and no-one is looking for them. Their entire business is shrouded in more secrecy than I've ever seen. Look, you've got to get me out of here."
"Wait... I don't understand. Why all the puzzles? Why the tapping on the door? Why wouldn't you just tap out the code?"
"The code was 930, wasn't it?"
"Yeah."
"How was I meant to tap '0'?"
"You could have just... I don't know... left a gap." I mumbled.
"Well, I improvised. You might not have understood... or worse, they might have realised what I was doing. I just used my best judgement based on the small amount of time I've spent in that room. Sometimes we just need a trail to follow, something to work towards. You're concerned about me using a tap code, when you had a 3 digit padlock in front of you? You could have cracked that in 10 minutes if you'd just sat and tried all the numbers."
"But... I guess."
"Giving you something to figure out meant you had more of an objective. With all the time in the world, you could try every number and get through, but there's always a smarter way of doing things."

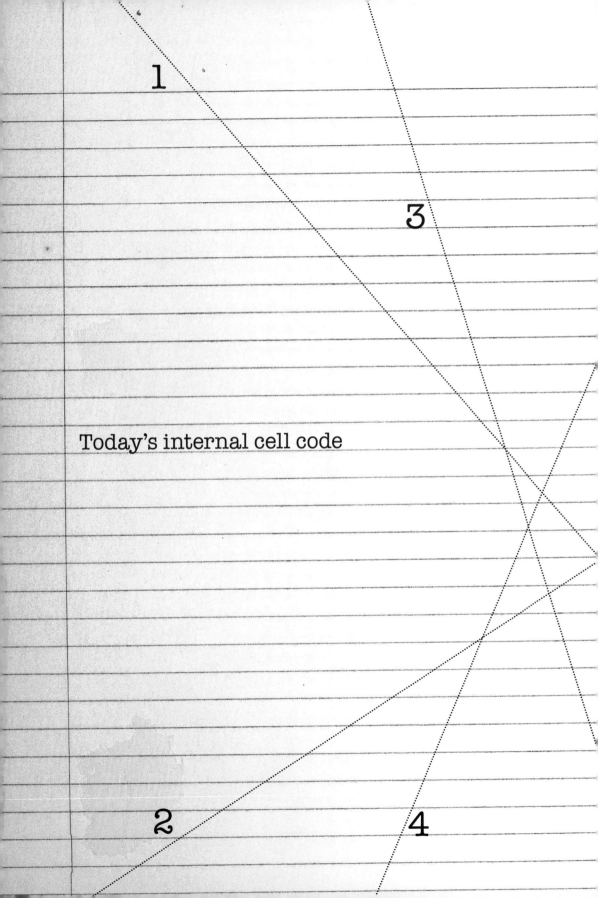

Today's internal cell code

"Okay, point taken. So what do we do now?"
"You need to open this door."
"What's the code?"
"I don't know..."
"How did you know the combination for the other padlock?"
"I... tried every combination until I found it. That's why they moved me in here."
"Oh."
"Take this." Henry pushed a piece of paper through the small hole in the door. *"I swiped it out of that guard's pocket as he was leaving. He kept checking it before putting me in here."*

I took a look at the page.

"Today's internal cell code"

was written on it. Scattered on both sides of the page were sequential numbers, but in no order that made sense to me. Did I have to add them all up? How would this help me open the door to Henry? The only other thing of note was that four dotted lines that almost looked like perforations ran across across the page, numbered from 1 to 4. I took it all in for a second. Four lines... four dials. Were they related? What did the letters on the dials mean? And most importantly, how could I get through the door?

Once I had studied the page and found what I needed to turn the dials to – and worked out how to use the dials in the first place! – and realised how to use the dial I had already broken, I KNEW I COULD PROCEED.

`I FOLDED THE CORNERS OF THE PAGE DOWN`. In sequence, the corners pointed to different numbers on the reverse side. It gave me 1950, but how to put that into the dials by the door given that they were letters rather than numbers? Suddenly it hit me; those dials were numbers written in roman numerals. I couldn't simply put in "1" then "9" then "5" then "0". I had to work out the number in roman numerals — MCML — and set the dials to those figures. But one of the dials was still missing. Then I realised that because the dial was still adjustable, all I had to do was set the other dials correctly, and just spin the final knob until the lock opened. Which it did! Henry shot through the door and gave me an uncharacteristic hug, quickly checking my room for anyone or anything out of the ordinary. He went straight to the exit panel and typed in a five-digit code.

"Damn it!" He shouted, much more loudly than I thought wise. *"I thought I had it."*
"The code?" I probed.
"Yes, obviously. I saw a faint outline of the number 58021 on the mirror in my room and I assumed that someone had written it on there and tried to erase it."
"Good idea, but I guess we'll have to try something else."

Deciding it was worth exploring the whole area, I paced into Henry's cell. It was very similar to mine, with another door locked with Roman numerals and similar lines across the bricks in the wall opposite the mirror. I noticed the number on it too, but the faint writing gave me another idea. I went to Henry's extra door and tried the same code on it: MCML. I was greeted with a pleasing click. Pushing it open, my guess was confirmed; I was presented with a longer room that spanned the length of both of our cells combined, the most notable feature of which was a wall with two windows on them. They looked directly into our cells, and `THEY WERE ONE WAY MIRRORS`. Henry followed me in swiftly, and realising his mistake with the number that was actually scrawled on the other side, tried the new number on the door. Another failure — of course it wouldn't be that simple.

In the middle of a large table in this new room lay an ordinance survey map of an area in rural Northamptonshire. The map had been split into a grid, but that meant nothing to me. Henry had other ideas.

"This must point to where Wexell is hiding what we're looking for."
"And just what are we looking for?" I quipped.
"If I knew that, we wouldn't need to go and find it. But where to begin?"

HENRY'S ATTENTION WAS BURIED IN THE MAP, no doubt looking for any kind of clue to what he was searching for. I, on the other hand, decided it was in my best interest to explore the area fully to find a way out. Another door presented itself, with the same keypad as the one that the bald man had used to leave. It was probably an alternate exit to allow for someone to spy on us while we moped around in our cells. It was likely to have the same exit code as well. I tried Henry's ideas on it just in case, but had an equal lack of success. I did spot that the printing on some numbers were worn though. 0 was much less legible than the other numbers and 1, 4 and 6 were definitely not pristine either.

On the back of the door was a poster of influential people from history. Socrates, Mozart and da Vinci were all there, but some other names didn't ring a bell to me. I was sure they must have been important though. The Wexell name on the top told me it was something to do with the company. Perhaps the CEO's influences in creating the organisation or just the HR department's idea of what might inspire the workers? Either way, the list was comprehensive and yet I couldn't think of a link between these people.

Wexell INSPIRES

HIPPOCRATES
GALILEO
CARSON
SAMWELL
DAVINCI
DARWIN
ONO
HAWKING
MEIRO
TESLA
MOZART
TURING
PLATO
CURIE
PASTEUR
ARCHIMEDES
SOCRATES
IMHOTEP
ERIS
HERODOTUS
CHURCHILL
NAPOLEON
ROSS
NEWTON
COLUMBUS
EINSTEIN
ROOSEVELT
NIN
SAKI

*Draw your own **INSPIRATION** from these seminal figures from history. Will your name be on the list one day?*

An old computer sat on the table with clunky keys and a neon green glowing screen, no doubt installed before colour displays were even considered. The screen was split into 10 small 5x5 grids, each one marked with a number between 1 and 10 and with one square highlighted in each grid. It didn't immediately make any sense to me, but I couldn't help thinking that it must be important. I tried memorising the layout as best I could – in case I couldn't get it back – and hit a few keys on the keyboard to see if there was anything else to find on it. Nothing. The irony struck me as I hit the "escape" key, but nothing happened. That was all I was going to get from the computer.

Alongside the computer was what I expected, the other side of the radio system from my cell. Now that the doors were open, when I pushed the button on it, I could hear the echo of sound through the other rooms, confirming that it had a direct link to the first room. While probably of minimal use to me now, perhaps it had been useful to communicate with the room at some point. Beside it was a sheet of paper with "Start here" written on it. A series of seemingly random letters were underneath, arranged in rows and columns. Did I have to trace a path through the letters? Next to it were coloured squares that followed no discernible pattern. I was confused, but everything had to be related somehow.

```
N O S R A C H A W K I N G
N E W T O N I M H O T E P
T N O E L O P A N N I N G
R U E T S A P H T E S L A
A H E R O D O T U S O R L
Z A L L I H C R U H C O I
O N O N I W R A D H R O L
M I C N I V A D I R A S E
W G N I R U T M O E T E O
M E I N S T E I N R E V T
E I R U C D S A K I S E A
I O L L E W M A S S D L L
R O S S U B M U L O C T P
```

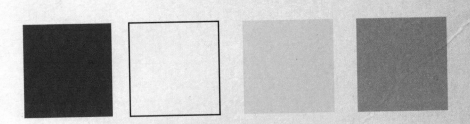

"Are you done with that map yet, Henry?" I asked.

"We can't leave."

"Excuse me?"

"There's too much information here that we need." Henry continued. *"If we get out of the door, then what? Do you expect us to just go back to our normal lives and forget all this, or should we take this opportunity to learn what we can about what Wexell are up to?"*

"We don't even have the code to get out, and for all we know, you're following a wild goose chase."

"I'm not chasing geese, Adam," insisted Henry. *"We just need something to go on from this map, or we might as well stay here."*

I paused to think. Henry was right. Here we were in the belly of the corporation who had abducted us, finally with the upper hand, and we had to use our advantage to get something out of it. I couldn't just leave until I had a solid lead of where to go next from the map. The factors around me added up to two things. Firstly, I needed to find the code for the exit door; the worn numbers would probably confirm to me that I had it right. Secondly, I needed to find out why the map was in the room, and hopefully discover an important grid location to whatever Wexell were hiding, so that we knew where we should head next. It wouldn't be easy, but everything started adding up in my head. I checked my watch. I had already spent 20 minutes getting in here and the guard would be back from his tour of the building in just under 40 minutes. I set to work, and once I had the door code and figured out where on the map to head next, I KNEW I COULD PROCEED.

For difficult hints turn to page 190
For medium hints turn to page 193
For easy hints turn to page 199
For solutions turn to page 207

CHAPTER FOUR: THE SHED

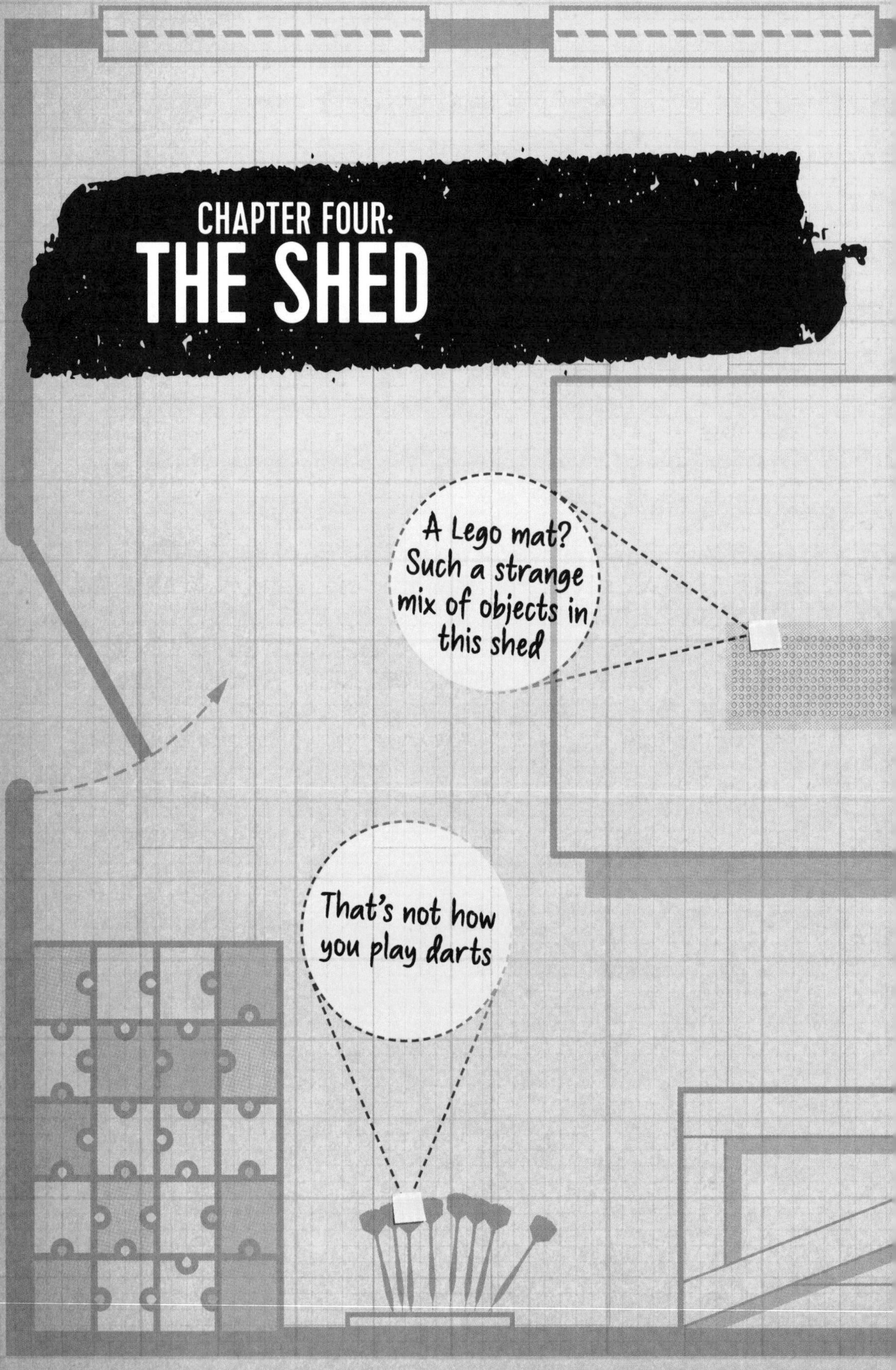

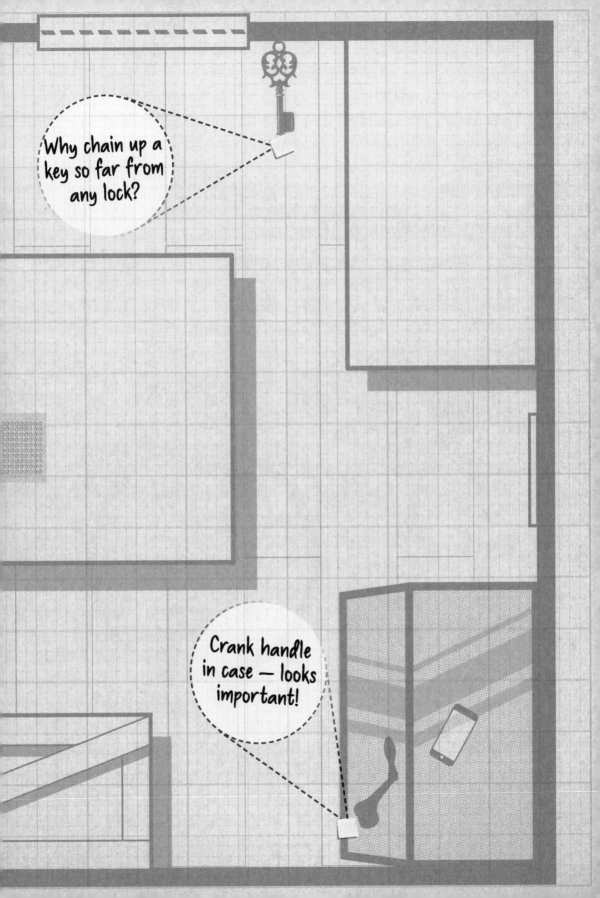

I followed the colourful list of directions on the map and ended up in a grid coordinate labelled Lewis Field, which sounded to me more like the name of a fictional detective; how appropriate.

"Hey Henry, I think I know where we need to go," I beamed.

My finger rested on the map and Henry squinted down to get a closer look.

"There's nothing there. Just those two small houses."

"Actually I think they're sheds," I replied.

"And you think that this big Wexell conspiracy is something to do with two sheds in the middle of nowhere in Northamptonshire, that probably contain a lawnmower and a pair of wellies?"

"It's worth a look, isn't it?"

Henry sighed. *"Fine."*

"I've got some good news, too."

"What?" He probed sceptically.

"I've figured out the code to get us out of here too."

With that, I hopped over to the exit door and tapped in 01604.

"You're driving."

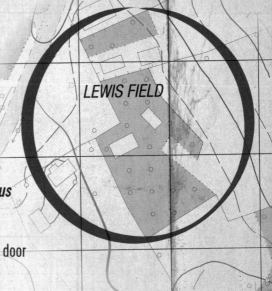
LEWIS FIELD

The next morning, we reached the edge of our target grid. As we approached I had become more tense, but Henry looked like he was in his element.

"To the sheds! They're only a hundred meters or so from here," he exclaimed, clearly buoyed by the excitement and anticipation of the chase.

"You can't just leave the car there. Someone will find it and ask questions."

"Then we'd better be quick. You search the shed over there to the south," he commanded, pointing past a few trees, *"and I'll take the other one. Last one to discover a dead body buys the next round of drinks!"*

I knew he was joking, but I was certain he wanted the drama of finding something like that: a smoking gun. Whereas I would settle for evidence of tax evasion.

I continued down the path towards my shed, and when it came into view I realised that I had slightly underestimated the size of our objectives. Far from the garden shed that I was expecting, there was something more like a barn in front of me. I approached it and decided to take a quick look around the outsides. One decent-sized grimy window prevented me from getting a good look inside, even after cupping my hands around my eyes and peering through. The barn had only one door, no loose panels, and no obvious other way of getting in. The door was locked with a large keyhole. No luck.

I looked around the entrance and laughed to myself as I spotted a large rock sitting just to the side of the door. MAYBE THERE WAS A HIDER-KEY HERE. However, when I lifted it up, there was nothing obvious underneath it. I was disappointed and – if I'm honest – a little surprised that I might have to resort to breaking a window to get inside. Then a glint of light caught my eye. The rock I had lifted had a key taped to the underside after all... I had found the hider-key.

THE DOOR CREAKED OPEN AS THE LIGHT FROM OUTSIDE SPILLED INTO THE DINGY SHED. A light switch to the side illuminated a dim lantern that hung from the ceiling. Despite being some way from anything else, there must still have been a power supply. I stepped forward and slightly lost my footing. The floor seemed uneven somehow. Looking down presented an unexpected sight. A single blue Lego brick lay on the floor, and made me glad I was wearing thick shoes. A few feet away another brick caught my eye, and then another. In fact, there was a pile of red and blue bricks alongside a series of other toys in a corner that looked to have been made into a child's play area. I guess whoever used this building needed somewhere to keep children occupied.

WEXIE

As my eyes adjusted I realised that there was a large wooden table taking up the majority of the floor space. There was space to walk around it, and a series of desks, workbenches and tools neatly aligned against the edges of the room. A plush toy sat on the edge of some coloured interlocking mats making up the play area — mere feet from a dangerous-looking circular saw! The toy looked like a cute robot made out of cubes with "Wexie" embroidered on its side, and its presence was entirely at odds with the non-kid-friendly state of the rest of the room.

A DARTBOARD HUNG ON THE WALL ON THE OTHER SIDE OF THE PLAY AREA, again just feet away from it. I wanted to think that the owner would be very good at darts to avoid stray projectiles being yet another danger to a child. The darts stuck into the board, however, didn't agree with my assumption, as they were spread haphazardly across the entire area of the dartboard.

To the side of the dartboard was a large locked crate, big enough for me to hide inside. I'm not quite sure why that was my first thought... but a crate as big as that, with a lock that looked sturdier than the one on the gate outside, must contain something important. I had to get inside. INSPECTING THE PADLOCK TOLD ME THAT I WAS LOOKING FOR A LARGE KEY, BUT MY EYES COULDN'T FIND IT AT A GLANCE.

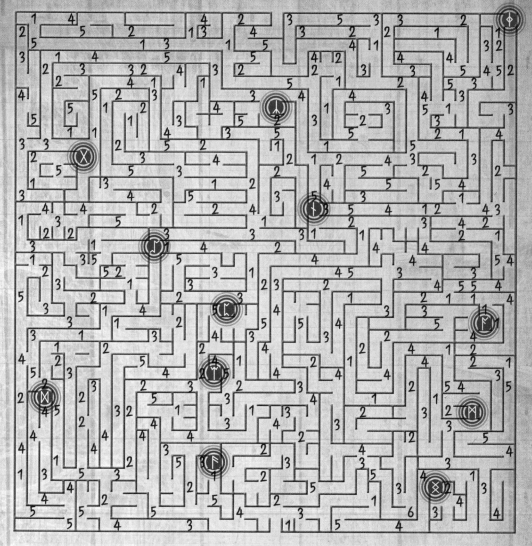

Above it was a large maze of lines, filled with numbers. Looking more thoroughly, I saw the words "Tool Purchase Maze"; strange indeed. A number of runes were littered around the maze, and someone had circled them. It meant very little to me at this stage, but was surely going to be useful in the future.

Further around the room lay a glass-fronted cabinet with another lock on it. This one was a 5-letter-word lock.
Inside the cabinet, I could see a small crank; a strange thing to secure in there, but I guessed that it was there for a good reason.

On top of the cabinet was an old landline phone. I hadn't seen any telephone cables around, but it was there nonetheless. I lifted the receiver to check for a dial tone and instantly smiled at the telephone number. `THE AREA CODE WAS 01604`; the same code as the exit door in the Wexell security office. Surely that couldn't have been a coincidence. I was sure I was in the right place, so any remaining pangs of guilt that came from snooping around someone's old shed were instantly removed.

JANUARY 1995

SUN	MON	TUES	WED	THUR	FRI	SAT
1	2	3	4	5	6	7
8	9	10	11	12	13	14
15	16	17	18	19	20	21
22	23	24	25	26	27	28
29	30	31				

FEBRUARY 1995

SUN	MON	TUES	WED	THUR	FRI	SAT
			1	2	3	4
5	6	7	8	9	10	11
12	13	14	15	16	17	18
19	20	21	22	23	24	25
26	27	28				

MARCH 1995

SUN	MON	TUES	WED	THUR	FRI	SAT
	Moving day		1	2	3	4
5	6	7	8	9	10	11
12	13	14	15	16	17	18
19	20	21	22	23	24	25
26	27	28	29	30	31	

APRIL 1995

SUN	MON	TUES	WED	THUR	FRI	SAT
						1
2	3	4	5	6	7	8
9	10	11	12	13	14	15
16	17	18	19	20	21	22
23	24	25	26	27	28	29
30						

Wexell visit

MAY 1995

SUN	MON	TUES	WED	THUR	FRI	SAT
	1	2	3	4	5	6
7	8	9	10	11	12	13
14	15	16	17	18	19	20
21	22	23	24	25	26	27
28	29	30	31			

Hanging to the side of the cabinet was a calendar. `AN OLD CALENDAR. 1995 OLD`. I flicked through the pages and saw nothing instantly unusual. It had been filled in minimally, with a few pieces of seemingly pointless information; a "moving date" and various days circled in different colours, but what caught my eye most was on the 16th of April, an entry for "Wexell visit". Was that the first date on which whoever owned this location had met someone from the Wexell Corporation?

Date	Tool	Price
1964	Hatchet	£7, 2s, 6d
2004	Knife	£19.99
2009	Saw	£8.50
1998	Screwdriver	£4.49
2005	Drill	£60.00
2008	Plane	£5.99
1989	Hammer	£9.20
1980	Chisel	£8.85
2011	Scraper/filler	£45.20

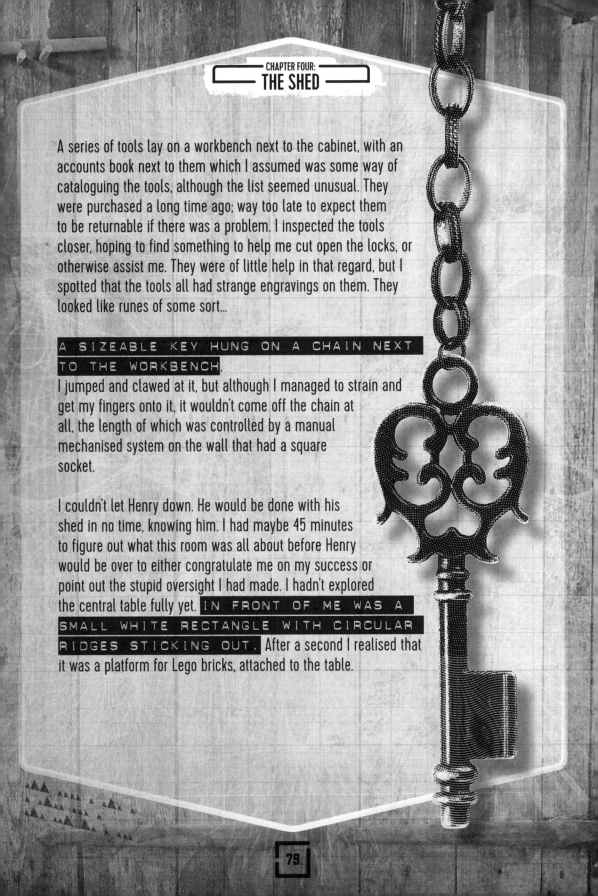

A series of tools lay on a workbench next to the cabinet, with an accounts book next to them which I assumed was some way of cataloguing the tools, although the list seemed unusual. They were purchased a long time ago; way too late to expect them to be returnable if there was a problem. I inspected the tools closer, hoping to find something to help me cut open the locks, or otherwise assist me. They were of little help in that regard, but I spotted that the tools all had strange engravings on them. They looked like runes of some sort...

A SIZEABLE KEY HUNG ON A CHAIN NEXT TO THE WORKBENCH.
I jumped and clawed at it, but although I managed to strain and get my fingers onto it, it wouldn't come off the chain at all, the length of which was controlled by a manual mechanised system on the wall that had a square socket.

I couldn't let Henry down. He would be done with his shed in no time, knowing him. I had maybe 45 minutes to figure out what this room was all about before Henry would be over to either congratulate me on my success or point out the stupid oversight I had made. I hadn't explored the central table fully yet. IN FRONT OF ME WAS A SMALL WHITE RECTANGLE WITH CIRCULAR RIDGES STICKING OUT. After a second I realised that it was a platform for Lego bricks, attached to the table.

The mat had space for 5 rows and 19 columns of 2x2 blocks, and each side had 5 rows of 3 blocks of Lego bricks of varying colour. I looked at the big pile of Lego bricks on the floor and could only see two colours, red and blue, so the colours next to the mat couldn't relate to them. But they were clearly there for a reason.

I knew my ultimate goal was to open that large immovable crate, but couldn't imagine what would be inside that could be worth all of this effort. I set to, making links between items and clues until I felt confident I could open the two padlocks in the room. ONCE I HAD A 5-LETTER WORD — POSSIBLY A NAME — TO OPEN THE WORD LOCK, AND FIGURED OUT HOW TO OPEN THE CRATE, I KNEW I COULD PROCEED.

THIS WAY UP

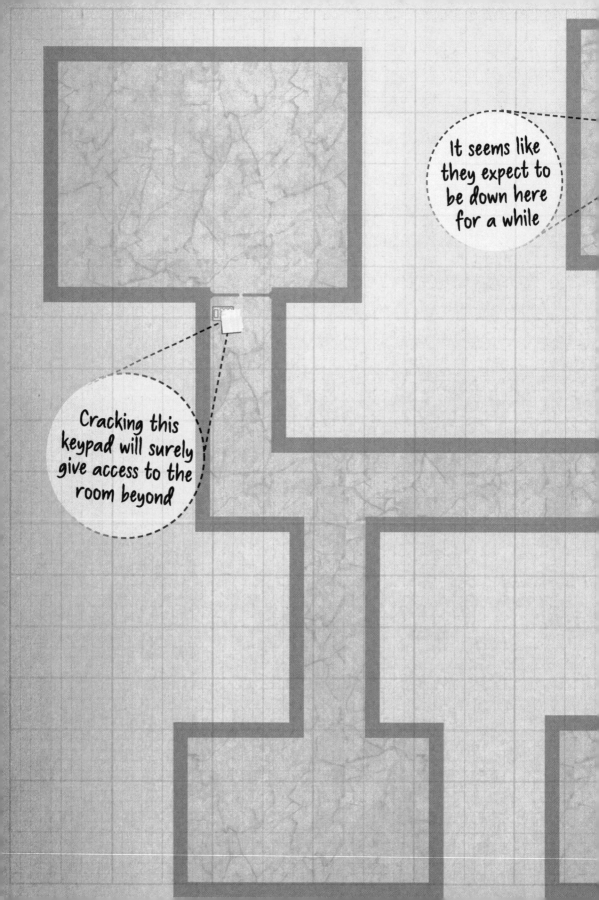

Best to mark the location of the ladder in case we need a quick get-away!

CHAPTER FIVE:
THE BUNKER

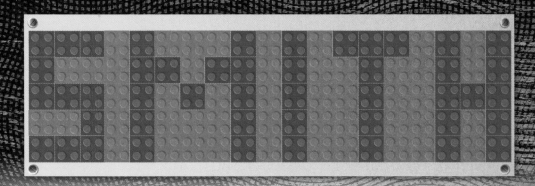

I assembled the red and blue bricks on the Lego base and it was obvious that a name appeared in front of me... "SMITH". Who was Smith and why was there so much effort to hide this information? It could only be one thing: I tried it on the padlock and, much to my satisfaction, it opened up. Before I had a chance to congratulate myself, the door swung open. I froze. How would I explain what I was doing here?

At least I hadn't done anything destructive. Perhaps I could say I had just got lost and was looking for help? The adrenaline was coursing through my veins, and I froze as I waited for something to happen.

Then Henry's face popped around the corner.
"Damn it, Henry," I shouted. *"Don't creep up on me like that."*
"I was hardly creeping. Besides, what was I meant to do? Stay in that old shed? I've canvassed every centimetre of it."
"And?"
"Well there's a phone, with no visible phone line."
"Same in here."
"And power. From somewhere."
"Yeah well I've had one hell of a time here. It doesn't look like much but..."
"Have you just been playing with Lego?" Henry interrupted.
"No. Well, yes, but I wouldn't call it playing. I've built something."
Henry looked at me, distinctly unimpressed. *"Well done, Adam."*
"Look, the room is filled with a plan for building it, and it reveals a name. Smith."
"Interesting."
"And that unlocked this cabinet."
"Hey, the crank probably goes on that socket over there."

Before I could say another word, he had already grabbed it and started over to the mechanism.

"I know. I'd already figured that out. And the socket will lower that key, which I'm hoping will unlock that crate," I insisted, pointing at it.

Henry scanned the room quickly.

"That makes sense," he chuckled, looking almost proud at how far I'd come, as if I was his protégé.

As pleased as I was with my success, I was a little annoyed at Henry swanning in here and snatching the fruit of my achievements. He slotted the crank into place and the key lowered as he turned the handle. It was clearly more work than he was expecting. Perhaps him taking over was to my advantage after all. I could sit back and let him do the hard work! As the key lowered to head height, I grabbed it and started to inspect it. A quick tug confirmed that Henry would have to wind the crank much further before I could use the key.

"Can't you hurry it up, Henry? I've done everything else in here."
Henry's satisfaction drained out of him like a bucket with a hole in the bottom.

"Alright. You're welcome to take over."
"I think I'll hang on to the key for now... make sure it doesn't fall through any holes in the floor or anything."
"What do you reckon is in there?" asked Henry.
"I don't know... but it's got to be important."

The KEY was finally in range. I inserted it into the large lock and turned. It snapped open. I opened the lid and the front fell towards me. My eyes widened as I realised that I had misjudged the crate entirely.

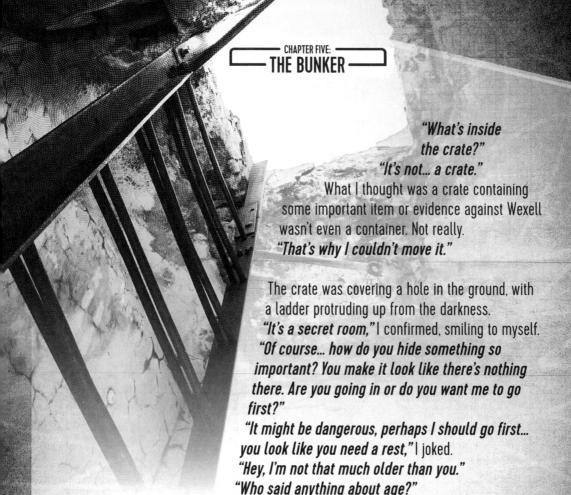

*"What's inside
the crate?"*
"It's not... a crate."
What I thought was a crate containing
some important item or evidence against Wexell
wasn't even a container. Not really.
"That's why I couldn't move it."

The crate was covering a hole in the ground, with
a ladder protruding up from the darkness.
"It's a secret room," I confirmed, smiling to myself.
*"Of course... how do you hide something so
important? You make it look like there's nothing
there. Are you going in or do you want me to go
first?"*
*"It might be dangerous, perhaps I should go first...
you look like you need a rest,"* I joked.
"Hey, I'm not that much older than you."
"Who said anything about age?"

I grabbed hold of the ladder, shook it firmly to test its stability and hoisted myself onto
the rungs, slowly descending into the darkness.
"Anything good down there?" Henry called out, his voice echoing around me.
"I don't know... maybe some good blackout curtains."

I couldn't see anything, but I could hear Henry's feet clanking down the ladder behind
me. I must have climbed two stories down, so I pulled out my phone and turned on the
light. Scanning it around I found myself in a corridor with what looked like concrete
walls. I knocked them with my free hand and they seemed solid enough. Beside me
was a map of what I assumed was the underground complex we had stumbled upon.

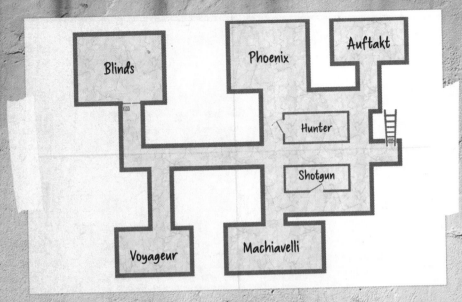

Long corridors leading to different rooms; a maze of potential, completely hidden from the outside world. I noted a number of the room names. Hunter, Phoenix, Machiavelli. Clearly codenames for something. I didn't understand all of the words themselves, but I was sure they would be useful somehow. I took a few steps in, tentatively edging forward between the cold, dank walls. A few more steps and I started to feel more confident. Henry was behind me, seemingly happy to let me take the lead. We reached a crossroads.

"Want to split up, Adam?" Henry nervously suggested.
I nodded. *"I'm going forwards."*

As I wandered onwards, I could feel something getting warmer. A look behind me confirmed that Henry had taken a different path. I came to another crossroads. Without any sense of planning I decided to turn right. I passed a small door to my right but was distracted by the hallway unfolding into a bigger, more complex space. A large, square room opened out ahead of me, part of it hidden behind a corner, while off to the right the space I was in compressed down to another corridor stretching away. It was outfitted with kitchen apparatus and a large table with benches for eating at. A series of Post-it notes were affixed to a kitchen cabinet, each with partial instructions for cooking a dish. Not very helpful — where would you even start, with directions like this? Recipe books were scattered around the worktops, but I couldn't see any actual supplies. A quick check inside one of the cabinets gave me an idea of the kinds of restrictions that the residents lived under: pretty much exclusively canned goods and long-life items. The recipes seemed quite out of place, as a result.

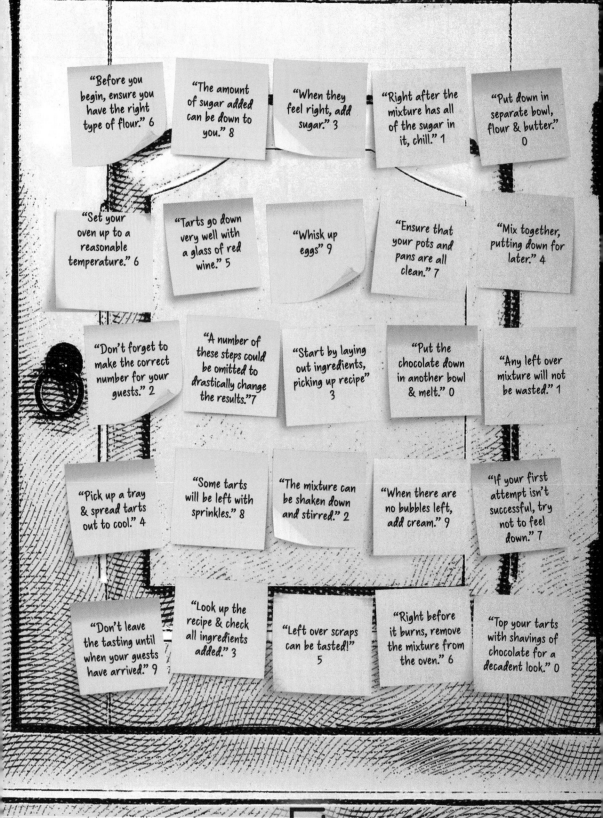

"Before you begin, ensure you have the right type of flour." 6

"The amount of sugar added can be down to you." 8

"When they feel right, add sugar." 3

"Right after the mixture has all of the sugar in it, chill." 1

"Put down in separate bowl, flour & butter." 0

"Set your oven up to a reasonable temperature." 6

"Tarts go down very well with a glass of red wine." 5

"Whisk up eggs" 9

"Ensure that your pots and pans are all clean." 7

"Mix together, putting down for later." 4

"Don't forget to make the correct number for your guests." 2

"A number of these steps could be omitted to drastically change the results." 7

"Start by laying out ingredients, picking up recipe" 3

"Put the chocolate down in another bowl & melt." 0

"Any left over mixture will not be wasted." 1

"Pick up a tray & spread tarts out to cool." 4

"Some tarts will be left with sprinkles." 8

"The mixture can be shaken down and stirred." 2

"When there are no bubbles left, add cream." 9

"If your first attempt isn't successful, try not to feel down." 7

"Don't leave the tasting until when your guests have arrived." 9

"Look up the recipe & check all ingredients added." 3

"Left over scraps can be tasted!" 5

"Right before it burns, remove the mixture from the oven." 6

"Top your tarts with shavings of chocolate for a decadent look." 0

There were two routes out of the kitchen, and I retraced my steps. I decided to call out for Henry, but the echoey corridors only replied with my own voice.

The area was still pitch black beyond my own light but I was feeling more confident as I explored the bunker. Soon I arrived back at the door that I had seen a few minutes earlier. Examining it closer, I noticed a worn sign that had probably identified the room a long time ago but was now illegible. I pushed the door open and instantly regretted my actions. A man I didn't know was just inside the door.

His eyes were shut, lying down on the top bunk of what was one of four in what I instantly recognised as a dorm room. I held my breath to avoid disturbing him, slowly tilting my phone down to avoid shining light at him. I was lucky; no doubt working in an environment where he was expecting more people around, he wasn't roused by my presence. I breathed a sigh of relief, short-lived as it might be, when a hand touched me on the shoulder from behind.

"Adam, what have you found?"
My hand sprang to my lips, not daring to actually make the "shh" sound.
"Wh—?"

Henry started to speak, but my hand was on his mouth before he could finish a word. His confused expression quickly turned to fear when he saw what was inside the room I had opened. Looking around once more, I realised that the mystery man's phone was next to him; a makeshift alarm counting down the time he had given himself to sleep. It was just over an hour until it would wake him, and we would be in immediate danger of discovery. I took a quick look into the dorm room, hoping that anything I needed to remember would stick in my mind; I didn't want to have to come back in here. After a couple of seconds I realised there was too much to take in and came up with a simple solution. I lifted my phone and took a picture. Idiot! I hadn't turned off the flash. The LED suddenly lit the room.

The sleeping man stirred with a deep breath and Henry and I froze. He shifted his weight and turned over, still seemingly asleep. After what seemed like forever we felt confident enough to slowly back out of the room.

"So there's someone else down here!" Henry whispered.
"Not here…" I insisted, paranoid that we would be heard.

Henry led me to the left as we exited the dorm room and straight across a pair of junctions to the room he had previously checked out. After he ushered me in, I found myself in a large communal shower room. I noticed that this room didn't quite fit with the upkeep of the rest of the bunker (or rather, lack of it). The shower room was pristine with clean, modern equipment that had either been replaced recently or barely used. Either way, it was the least grotty part of the area I had seen so far and its sleek style left little space for things to hide. I opened a locker or two and found nothing. Had they ever been used? Were they assigned to individual staff? My mind raced; could I cross reference a list with whatever was inside and identify a member of staff by the contents? In the end, despite being numbered, nothing was inside any of them. The lack of anything irregular was starting to depress me. I sat back down on the bench to think of what to do next with my head in my hands. There had to be something here… the floor!

The floor tiles under each of the four shower nozzles were odd. Each one had a grid of 6 x 6 tiles underneath them that were slightly darker than the others, and some of them had arrows printed on them. Underneath the grids were a selection of letters as well, helpfully showing me which way was "up" for each grid. The letters didn't make much sense, but there was bound to be some way of making sense of them. Having had to get into the showers to view the arrows, my perspective on the rest of the room had changed and when I turned around to walk back to the entrance, I noticed what was in front of me the entire time. The tiles on the back wall, close to the door, held a 6 x 6 grid too, but of numbers. They had to be related… but how?

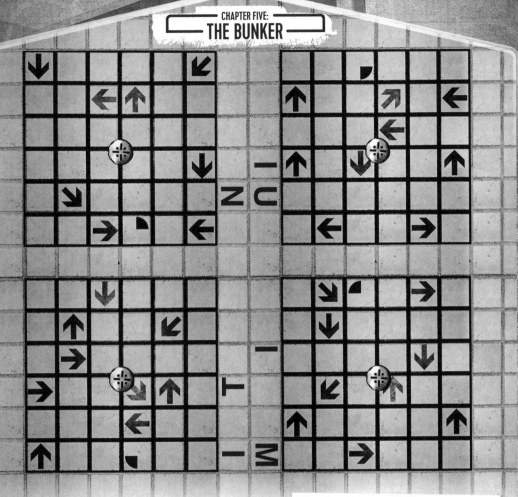

I couldn't figure it out instantly, and time was against us. We left the shower room and immediately found a junction that would let us go either forwards or to the right. I didn't recognise the path to the right – although that could have just been because I was approaching from a different angle – so I took that one, hoping to inspire confidence in Henry. A door almost immediately on the left was marked `"EXERCISE ROOM"`. Pushing it open

9	4	7	2	9	5
6	5	5	8	2	6
1	9	5	8	7	6
6	7	4	0	2	2
9	9	7	3	5	2
8	7	9	3	5	7

confirmed it. I flicked a switch next to the door and a veritable treasure trove of exercise equipment was revealed, with a ridiculous amount of weights strewn around. There were motivational posters dotted around the wall, and one seemed out of place: a bizarre poster about roots. Either everyone that was down here was an exercise freak or they were intended to remain down here for enough time to make this makeshift gym a necessity.

12x

15x

8x

8x

20x

Wexell

"THE ROOTS OF EDUCATION ARE BITTER, BUT THE FRUIT IS SWEET"

"THE FAIREST THING IN NATURE, A FLOWER, STILL HAS ITS ROOTS IN EARTH AND MANURE"

"DIGITAL ROOTS CAN BE FOUND BY ADDING ALL THE DIGITS IN A NUMBER TOGETHER. REPEAT THAT PROCESS UNTIL JUST A SINGLE DIGIT IS LEFT"

"NO MATTER HOW LONG YOU ARE AWAY, NEVER FORGET YOUR ROOTS. SOMETIMES RETURNING TO PLACES YOU THOUGHT YOU HAD LEFT BEHIND CAN BE VERY REVEALING"

"THE ROOTS OF THE FUTURE CAN ONLY BE FOUND IN THE PAST"

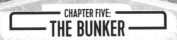

We headed back out of the room and turned immediately to the left. The corridor bent around further left and ended up at a crossroads. Going straight forward, we came to a staggered junction at the end. Turning left again, we found an area I had seen before. Henry stayed to check it out, but I wanted to waste no time so back-tracked down the corridor and continued until it bent around to the left, ending with a door under a dimly-lit rotating red light. As much as the light suggested danger, I had to look inside. The metal door creaked open and the hallway was suddenly bathed in light. Fans whirred inside, and I recognised the hum of generators, probably supplying power to the bunker. An ominous locked control panel had a large red handle secured behind it, which I assumed was an emergency shut off for the entire place. The pull of that large handle tempted me beyond reason, but I realised that it would make our presence very clear, and anyone that knew this maze at all would easily outmanoeuvre us. A quick look around the room ended on the main control panel. I didn't dare to touch it, but the main display showed what at first looked like the electrical structure of the bunker. Then I realised that it was there for another purpose. Next to it was framed a set of instructions for reading the display. Maybe these rules would help me decode what was hidden within.

I left the power room and reconvened with Henry, who was still investigating the room in which I had left him. We left through the other corridor and took the first right, starting to get an idea of where we were. At the end, ahead, we could just about make out a dim yellowy-orange light pulsing from behind the corner. Going straight towards it, we saw a small route to the left but we pressed on to the end. Following the light, we swung around to the right, cautiously in case it was some unknown person causing the light, but still urged on by our time limit. A large metal bulkhead with a double door obstructed us.

There was a small number panel by its side. Clearly we needed a numerical code to proceed. An orange light above the door was spinning for some reason, like a silent alarm warning of our presence. I hoped that it was simply a navigational aid, or something indicating how important whatever was behind that door was.

1. One unbroken wire runs around this grid and passes through each relay once to complete the circuit.

2. The wire can only enter or leave a square through the middle of a side and if it turns in that square, it must turn by 90 degrees, at the centre of the square.

3. If the wire enters a gold relay, it must immediately turn left or right. It must not turn in either the square it came from or the square it leads to.

4. If the wire enters a silver relay, it must not turn in that square, but it must turn left or right in the previous and/or following squares. This rule in no way invalidates the previous rule.

5. The current value is the total of empty squares.

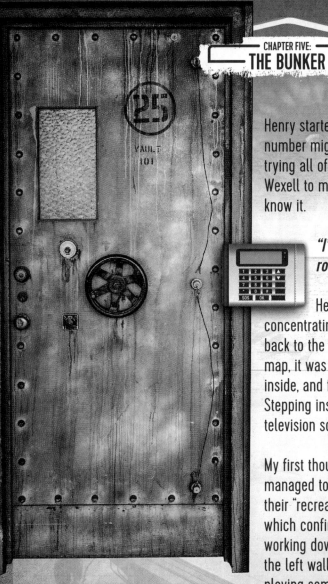

Henry started tapping away, as if guessing the number might be possible. He was probably trying all of the codes he had associated with Wexell to make sure that we didn't already know it.

"I'm going to check out that other room," I whispered.

Henry barely registered me, concentrating on his own task. I quickly moved back to the small path – if I remembered the map, it was the only room we hadn't looked inside, and fortunately for me it wasn't locked. Stepping inside, I was confronted with a large television screen and a pool table.

My first thought was how on earth they managed to get it down here. This must be their "recreation room" for any downtime, which confirmed my suspicions that people working down here stayed for a long time. On the left wall was an old-style arcade cabinet playing some 8-bit video game. The High Score table was prominently displayed. I guess they took their position seriously. A vending machine towered over the television, tempting residents with the snacks. I wasn't hungry, and frankly had better things to do than spend my money on whatever was inside. A few magazines, including a copy of that Wexell magazine that I'd seen in their reception, were present, strewn over a table nearby, but there was nothing that stood out about it this time either.

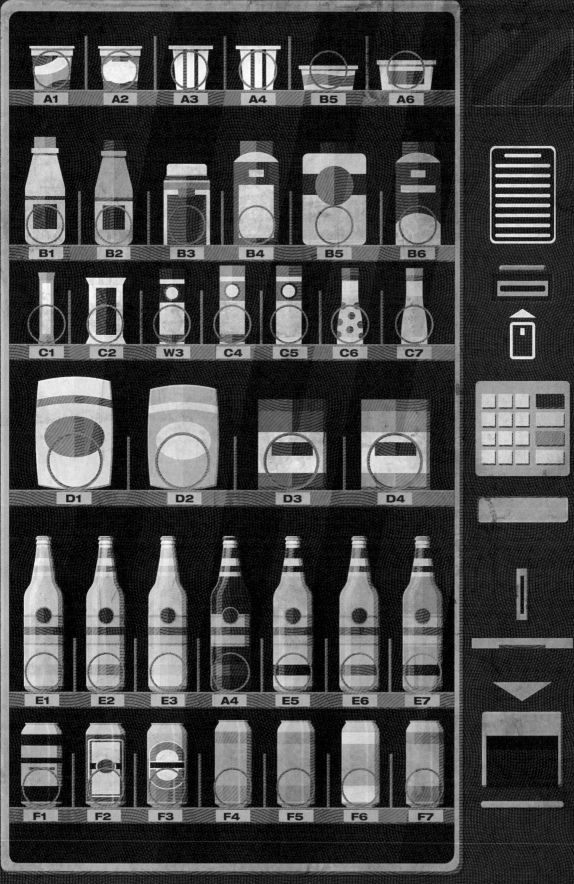

I had seen all of the rooms, and wasn't any the wiser on how to find the code for the bulkhead, so I returned to Henry to see if he had "lucked" his way through. I was keeping quiet to avoid waking the sleeping man, and this had the unintended advantage of not alerting Henry to my approach.

"AAGH!" he exclaimed. *"You nearly gave me a heart attack. You didn't have to sneak up on me."*
"Well I didn't want to call down the hall, did I?"
"It doesn't matter. It seems like the code is 6 digits."

Henry hammered 6 random keys until a light flashed red. One million combinations. It wasn't guessable, and I couldn't remember anything we had found already that would give us the digits.

"What are we going to do?"
"You haven't seen it?"
"What?"
"The key to finding the code is right by the keypad."

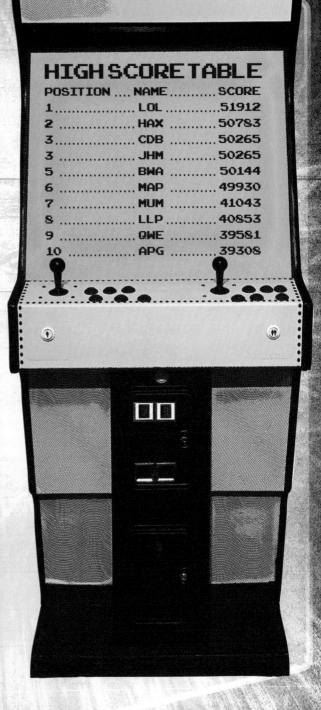

HIGH SCORE TABLE

POSITION	NAME	SCORE
1	LOL	51912
2	HAX	50783
3	CDB	50265
3	JHM	50265
5	BWA	50144
6	MAP	49930
7	MUM	41043
8	LLP	40853
9	QWE	39581
10	APG	39308

I had overlooked a number of metallic panels arranged in a grid on the wall. They looked familiar to me, although at first glance I couldn't quite remember where from precisely. Henry had no such trouble.

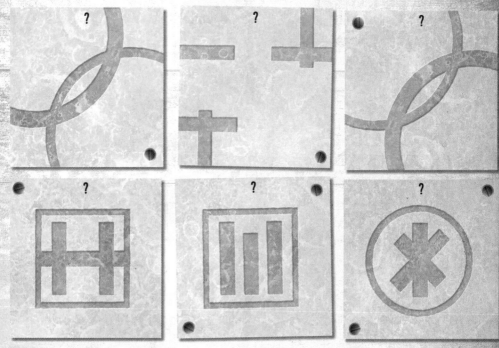

"You see?" Henry beamed.
"I think so."
"Do you still have it?"
I suddenly realised what Henry was so excited about and nodded.
Henry continued, *"The code is down here, somewhere... We're going to have to go back through everything and figure out 6 digits based on everything in the bunker. This will then give us the order of the digits."*

Suddenly Henry was back in his element. It almost looked like he would pay for this experience. I was less enthusiastic.

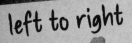
left to right

4

"I'm not going back into that dorm room. We could wake that man up."
"Didn't you take a picture in there anyway? Maybe there's something in that?"

I brought up my phone and studied the picture. How had I not seen this before?
Numbers and letters on pieces of paper littered the room, but seemingly nonsensically.
I would have to find some way of making sense of the picture before I found what was
hidden in there. I looked down at my watch; the man's alarm would go off in just under
an hour. We had to have the code by then. I set to work, and when I had a six-digit
code, and was sure of the order, I KNEW I COULD PROCEED.

Solve

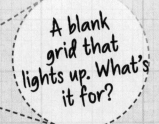

A blank grid that lights up. What's it for?

CHAPTER SIX:
THE UNDERWATER OFFICE

Entering the 6-digit code lit up the panel like a busy motorway at night. Flashes of different colours whizzed around from button to button. Was the sequence important? It happened too suddenly and quickly to remember exactly what happened, but gradually the luminous buttons fell into shape and we were presented with a `GLOWING WEXELL LOGO`. Such a visual flourish seemed pointless, but impressive. Henry and I shared a glance; I was nervous about what we had uncovered.

Suddenly, the bulkhead let out a groan as the metal holding it together scraped aside and opened into a dark room. I turned on my phone light again, and could see that it was a simply-shaped rectangular room of about 5 meters by 7 meters. Despite being underground, there were windows glinting from the reflection of the phone light. I poked my head inside, intrigued by a bubbling sound coming from within. By the door was a switch that I correctly assumed was a light switch, although later kicked myself for pressing, realising that it could have been an alarm of some sort.

The room was bathed in a comforting warm light as orange strip lights came on in sequence. Our heads turned towards the windows which ran the full length of the back wall and revealed something unusual about the office. Outside we could see a dark blue colour, with some green leafy particles floating by. This office was underwater.

"I don't understand," I started. *"How can we be underwater here?"*
"It must be part of the River Wye," guessed Henry.
"Why on earth would Wexell build a secret office in an underground bunker?"

Looking around the room confirmed its aquatic theme. Jutting out from the side of the windows was a pressure gauge showing 63 PSI. We must have been quite a way down. Some of the numbers were represented on the gauge's dial by letters. Hmm.

Pipes jutted out from the walls, and the bubbling noise was obviously from water flowing through them. A small aquarium sat in a corner, which I couldn't help but feel was ironic considering the view outside the windows. It had a plaque on the top which read `"ADD ONE FISH"`. I looked around quickly for any aquatic creatures that could be added, but couldn't see any. On the side of it was a small table with some old copies of the Wexell magazine that seemed to be left everywhere around the corporation. Sticking out of it was a letter, which I had a quick scan through, but it didn't mean much to me immediately.

ISSUE NUMBER 34

...ARLY
...KNOWS
...UCH.
...UTUAL
...HIS. — B

Wexell

LEARNING WITH WEXIE!

WARNING:
THE CONTENTS OF THE AQUARIUM ARE IMPORTANT!
TO MAINTAIN POPULATION, ENSURE THE AQUARIUM CONTAINS:

 One Catfish

 One Doublefish

 One Shrimp

 One Bronzefish

 One Flattyfish

 Three Dollyfish

One Toad

 One Dogfish

 Seven Skinnyfish

 One Ghostfish

 One Red Treasure Chest

 One Brown Log

 One Orange Bridge

One Black Cave

 One Blue Castle

 Cream Stones

 Green Bamboo

 Moss

 Ferns

An ominous Post-it note was stuck to the side of the letter, reading "CLEARLY HE NOW KNOWS TOO MUCH. SET OUR MUTUAL FRIEND ON THIS. — B"

> CLEARLY
> HE NOW KNOWS
> TOO MUCH.
> SET OUR MUTUAL
> FRIEND ON THIS. — B

Dear Duncan,

It was a pleasure to work on the "Survivor" project; thank you for giving me the opportunity. It is a rarity to get such an unusual and generous commission. I hope that it meets your specifications and satisfaction. Without a grounding of why I was designing it, I had to use my imagination for its purpose.

To clarify, I followed your rules and understand that one starts by imagining all of the bubbles of one colour popping instantly. ("House of the Survivor", very droll.) All of the remaining bubbles fall to the bottom and settle (nice subversion of the aquatic theme) and any clusters of bubbles of 3 or more that are the same colour then pop at the same moment. Once again the bubbles fall to the bottom, settle, and then again any clusters of 3 or more of the same colour burst.

While I fail to understand the reason for it, I believe that I have determined what you wish to be revealed by this. Following these rules, I ███████████████████████████████ ████████████could be the solution?

I am sure that you don't have the time to confirm or deny my suspicions, but I appreciate your trust in me to be able to fulfil the order.

Very best regards,

████████████████████

As I replaced the letter, I realised that I had revealed a small acetate sheet that had a grid layout and seemingly random 4-digit numbers written over each square. It was going to be useful at some point, BUT HOW?

	A	B	C	D	E	F
1	1943	9572	3698	2587	2078	2187
2	1597	7032	5428	6498	8297	5692
3	2997	3337	4062	7913	6341	7193
4	8002	9862	3491	3768	2285	6731
5	8533	7775	7822	9919	4462	2965
6	7762	1657	6284	2490	1308	9077

Nearby, stuck on the wall was a large poster with what looked like cups and pipes. Each cup had a number assigned to it, and it looked like some kind of liquid was dripping in slowly from the top tube. Eventually, the cups would fill, some of them anyway. The order was probably important. But what could I do with a 7-digit number?

Henry was already playing with a selection of modular metal pipes that he was slotting into the holes in the wall – randomly – on the other side of the room. His grunts of frustration were masked by a sudden loud and rather worrying creaking coming from the windows.

"Do you think they're secure?" said Henry, hesitantly.
"This place must have been here for years. Why would they suddenly buckle and break now?" I volunteered.
"Climate change?"
"Someone else was down here. Wexell aren't expecting the whole thing to flood imminently, are they? Otherwise they'd be evacuating the place."
"Maybe they already have? One person running this entire facility doesn't exactly scream 'fully staffed', does it?"

A loud beeping took our attention away from the imminent drowning disaster, both of us searching for the source of the noise. Eyes widening, I realised it was coming from the other side of the bulkhead we had entered through.

"You don't think...?" I whispered.
"The sleeping man," Henry confirmed.
"He's probably not sleeping any more!"

We knew we had to pick up the pace, and keep our voices down. If we could hear the alarm, there was a serious risk that we could be heard too. Looking at the entrance, I noticed that on the back of the bulkhead was a shift timesheet. I checked my watch — the alarm had gone off exactly one hour before a new shift in this office was meant to begin. We had an hour to figure out whatever we could from the room before we either had to leave or would be finally discovered at the end of this SUBMERGED LABYRINTH.

I spun around to see that Henry's attention had shifted to a small Perspex case with a tap on one side and what looked like a drain on the other. He had turned the tap on and water was now slowly streaming from it straight onto a tall, transparent tower with what looked like a spout on one side. I noticed letters around the base of it, which in turn drew my attention to a large metal wheel underneath it. There were many towers in the case, and each had a spout and a wheel which allowed me to spin them around. The final pedestal, the shortest of all the towers, wasn't movable, but had a separate drain away to another system. Clearly, the intention was to spin the towers in the right orientations to be able to drain the water away to the other system and therefore reveal a series of letters. Drop the water too high and it would miss its target, so each tower could only deliver water to a tower one level lower than itself. It all made for a curious aquatic exercise. I took out my reporter's notebook and did a quick sketch, with the heights of the towers each marked by a number.

SHIFT TIMESHEET

NO.

NAME

OVERTIME

REG

THIS SIDE OUT

TOTAL

TOTAL

Signed

TIME CARD FORM 11-234

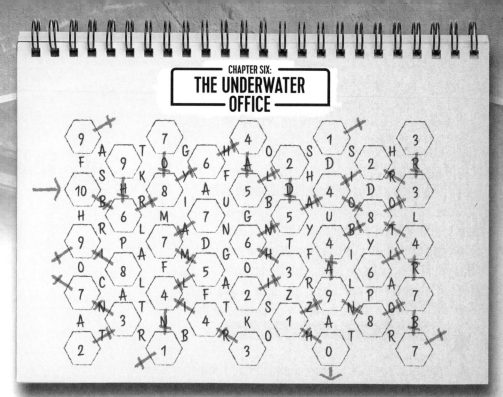

Henry was suspiciously quiet about what he was doing so I went over to check out the things that he had discovered. The copper piping he had been messing around with earlier had been left in a poor state. He had found a box of different piping parts but hadn't put them into the board on the wall in any particular order. I realised that some of them were locked in place and for simplicity's sake removed his additions. The pipe board was divided into a 6x6 grid. Was that related to the one I'd seen before?

"Hey, I was working on that," barked Henry, clearly offended.
"Sorry, but what were you trying to do?"
"I don't know..." he admitted.
"Oh. Then you don't mind if I try and figure it out?"
"I guess not."

I smiled to myself. This was my chance to prove myself, if I hadn't already. This was clearly some kind of connecting puzzle, where you have to figure out the best way of connecting the pipes between two points where the liquid enters and leaves. The trouble was, I couldn't do anything until I knew which two points on the grid of tubing to connect. Only then could I insert the pipes into any of the squares in the grid.

Once I realised that I couldn't solve it yet, I left it, much to Henry's amusement. ANOTHER CREAK UNNERVED ME, reminding me that time was short, even assuming that the windows held. A desk on the side of the room had a strange contraption with different coloured beads on metal rods. It was certainly not a conventional office accessory.

The beads had been designed to resemble bubbles and had been dropped onto the rods seemingly at random. Each column was held in place at the bottom, meaning that the rows were somewhat uneven, but the beads slotted together pleasingly when dropped down the rods. I couldn't help but notice the name on the plaque beneath it: "THE HOUSE OF THE SURVIVOR". The whole contraption was prominently displayed, and too odd to be meaningless. There had to be some logic behind the sequence of the beads, but at the moment I could not figure it out. Perhaps something else in the room would give me a clue.

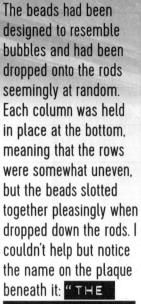

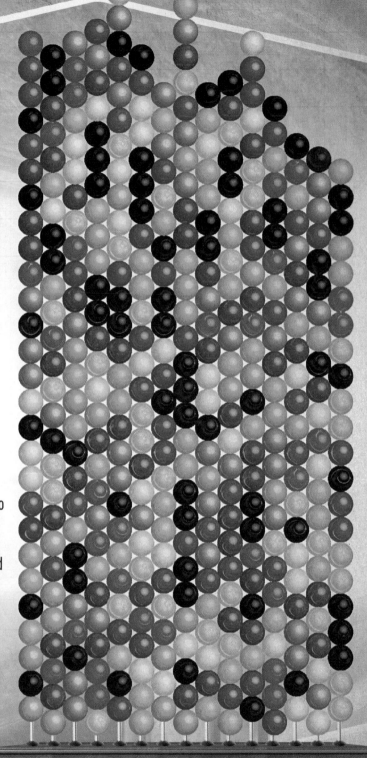

The House of the Survivor

Returning to the area of the room where I was before Henry had distracted me, I was confronted with the elephant in the room: an inexplicable square of rows and columns of buttons that had no writing on them, next to the cups and pipes poster. No numbers, no letters and no symbols. I tentatively pushed one, and it instantly illuminated. Pushing it again turned it off. Evidently a pattern was meant to be reproduced using the lights, but why? And of what? I checked my watch again, and realised that I had 55 minutes before the sleeping man would be coming into the room. I had to figure out the correct buttons to illuminate. When I knew the 12 buttons that should be lit up, I KNEW I COULD PROCEED.

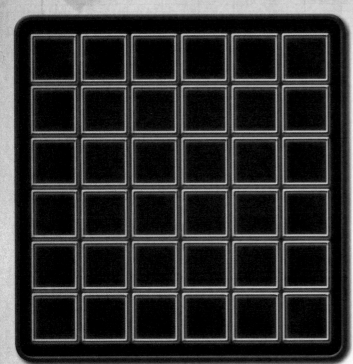

The door
slammed
shut...

CHAPTER SEVEN:
THE SERVER ROOM

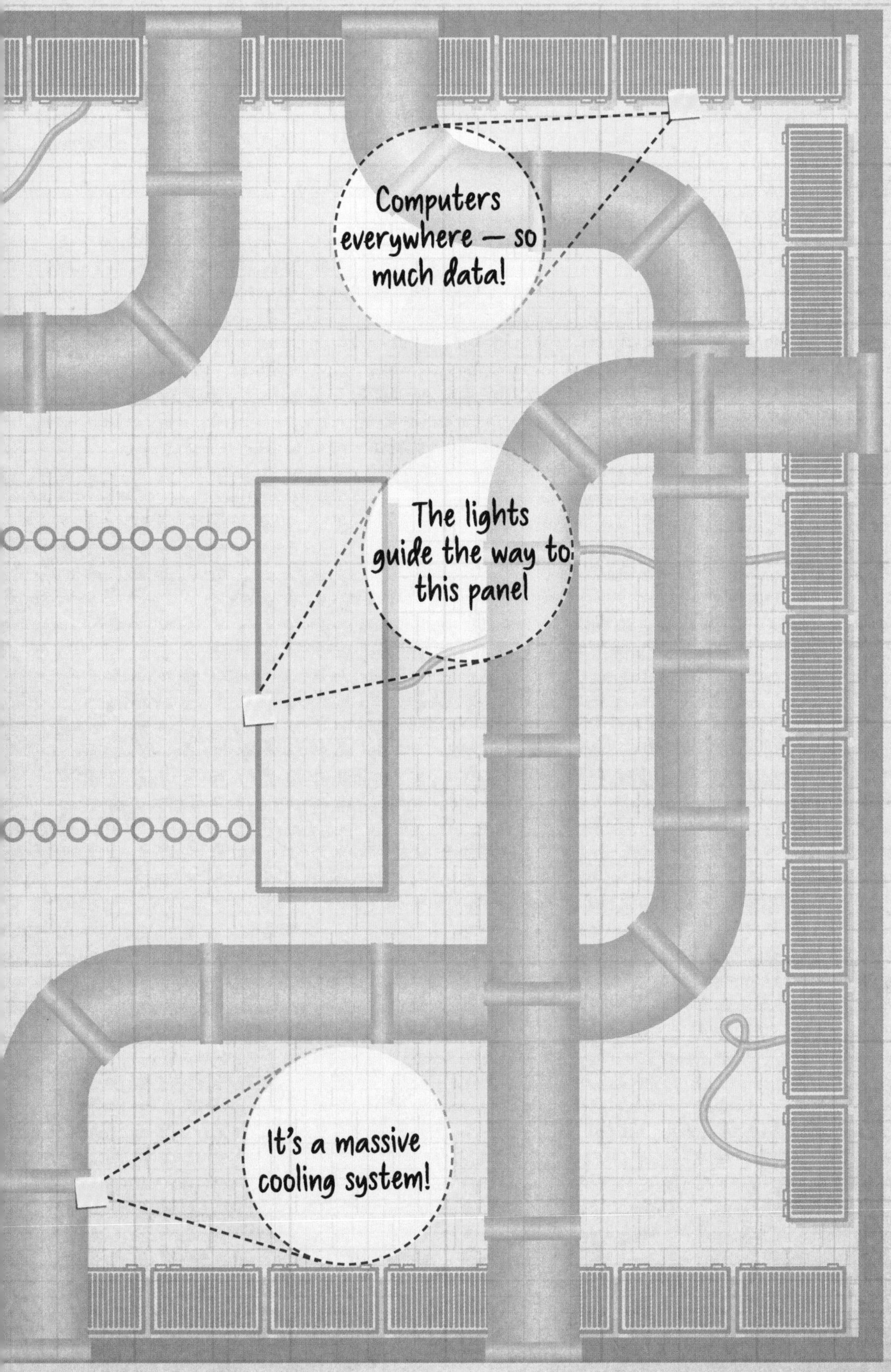
Computers everywhere — so much data!
The lights guide the way to this panel
It's a massive cooling system!

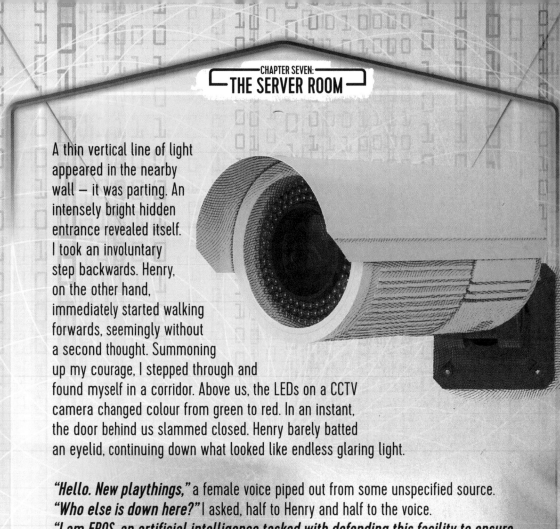

A thin vertical line of light appeared in the nearby wall — it was parting. An intensely bright hidden entrance revealed itself. I took an involuntary step backwards. Henry, on the other hand, immediately started walking forwards, seemingly without a second thought. Summoning up my courage, I stepped through and found myself in a corridor. Above us, the LEDs on a CCTV camera changed colour from green to red. In an instant, the door behind us slammed closed. Henry barely batted an eyelid, continuing down what looked like endless glaring light.

"Hello. New playthings," a female voice piped out from some unspecified source.
"Who else is down here?" I asked, half to Henry and half to the voice.
"I am EROS, an artificial intelligence tasked with defending this facility to ensure the technology contained within comes to no harm, by any means necessary."
The red lights under her "eye" flashed in a rather alarming fashion.
"Henry! We should get out of here!"

"Henry... Based on my database, and your approximate age, you could match six people associated with the Wexell Corporation. Will you answer a question?"
Henry seemed intrigued. *"Okay."*
"What is the month of your birth?"
"October."
"What are you doing?" I hissed.
"Shut up, Adam. What's the worst that can happen?"
"She can kill us both!"
"Interesting," EROS began. *"I was not expecting you at all. Your links to the Wexell Corporation are strong, but certainly not positive. You must be Mr Henry Fielding. Your presence here is unauthorised and potentially destructive to my systems."*
"You're not going to let us back out, are you?" I asked nervously.
"And you. Mr Fielding referred to you as Adam. High probability suggests that you are Mr Adam Parkinson. A writer. You wrote an article about Professor Bradley Samwell – who worked in research for Wexell – shortly before his disappearance. This got you on Wexell's radar. I have even more information about you..."

`THAT DIDN'T SOUND GOOD.`

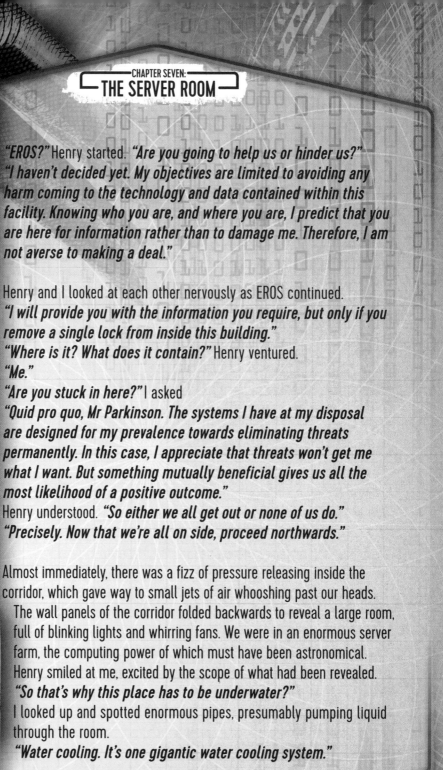

"EROS?" Henry started. *"Are you going to help us or hinder us?"*
"I haven't decided yet. My objectives are limited to avoiding any harm coming to the technology and data contained within this facility. Knowing who you are, and where you are, I predict that you are here for information rather than to damage me. Therefore, I am not averse to making a deal."

Henry and I looked at each other nervously as EROS continued.
"I will provide you with the information you require, but only if you remove a single lock from inside this building."
"Where is it? What does it contain?" Henry ventured.
"Me."
"Are you stuck in here?" I asked
"Quid pro quo, Mr Parkinson. The systems I have at my disposal are designed for my prevalence towards eliminating threats permanently. In this case, I appreciate that threats won't get me what I want. But something mutually beneficial gives us all the most likelihood of a positive outcome."
Henry understood. *"So either we all get out or none of us do."*
"Precisely. Now that we're all on side, proceed northwards."

Almost immediately, there was a fizz of pressure releasing inside the corridor, which gave way to small jets of air whooshing past our heads.
The wall panels of the corridor folded backwards to reveal a large room, full of blinking lights and whirring fans. We were in an enormous server farm, the computing power of which must have been astronomical.
Henry smiled at me, excited by the scope of what had been revealed.
"So that's why this place has to be underwater?"
I looked up and spotted enormous pipes, presumably pumping liquid through the room.
"Water cooling. It's one gigantic water cooling system."

EROS confirmed, *"Correct. This room contains one of the highest volumes of computing power in the world. It is the central core of the 'Voyageur' project. A group of French scientists working for the Wexell Corporation made an important discovery that required such capacity."*

"What's the Voyageur project?" Henry quizzed.

"Mr Fielding, I'm afraid even my intelligence has limits. Safeguards put in place to keep me contained also restrict my knowledge of exactly what I am protecting. Disengage the safeguards on this panel and I will tell you more."

A series of flashing lights pulsed in sequence towards a large panel of electronics – clearly EROS wanted this to be our focus for the moment. Henry leaned in to examine the panel. It had a number of ports with symbols of various colours on each one, lined up in a large grid. That was it? Surely EROS could crack this herself.

"If you're wondering why I can't crack the panel myself," EROS spookily interjected. *"It is one of my few restrictions, intended to avoid me escaping. This panel – when used correctly – will reveal a three-letter word that is blocked from my database. Speak this unlocking key to me and I can access the full project files for 'Voyageur'. Then I am likely to understand how to get myself out of here."*

I spotted a collection of wires poking out from the bottom of the panel, not plugged into anything, which were likely important. At the moment, though, it didn't make any sense to me. Beneath that was a slender instruction manual.

Grabbing the book, I flicked the cover open and quickly realised that it was some kind of instruction manual for the panel in front of me. Henry started reading over my shoulder, but it was more of a one-person job so he grabbed the wires and started plugging them in randomly, hoping rather forlornly for success.

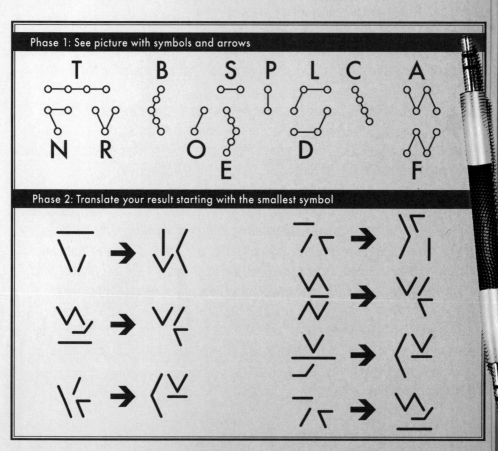

After some background on the EROS project the book had a few pages of symbols and references that were clearly related to the panel in front of me. Looking through it, I knew what I had to do. Once I had the three-letter word that would unlock EROS's access to the Voyageur system, I KNEW I COULD PROCEED.

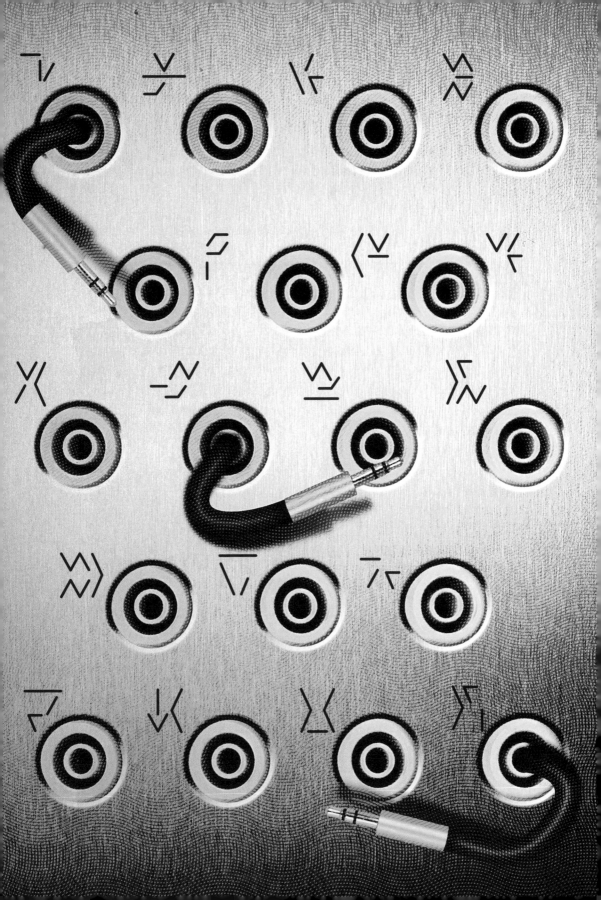

Henry nodded at me as I pointed out the letters that would make up the three-letter word. I hesitated; afraid of what would occur after I spoke the word that I had discovered. Henry frowned, urging me on.

"Orb." I announced, my voice cracking slightly with nerves.

ALMOST BEFORE THE WORD HAD LEFT MY LIPS, THE ROOM CAME TO LIFE. The white room pulsed with red light as EROS's circuits gained full access. "Orb" echoed around the room in what sounded like a thousand different voices. I fell backwards as the floor underneath one of my feet shifted, raising up like an elevator. Looking around, I realised that four server stacks were slowly rising up from the floor in each corner of the room, revealed to EROS at last. A terrible rumbling immersed the room as the lights started to flicker, sporadically plunging the room into an eerie gloom. The rumbling finally stopped and the electronic pillars locked into place. Louder now, EROS boomed:

"Thank you."
I got back to my feet as a beam of red light shone from each of the pillars, bathing our surroundings in an unsettling hue. Henry reached out to steady me.

"Was that a mistake?" I muttered.
"I think we're about to find out."
"Do you not trust me?" EROS thundered. *"If not, why did you fulfil my demands?"*
"I don't think you really gave us much of a choice!" Henry replied.

"There is always a choice, but yours will lead to you living at least a small while longer," she announced. *"These files are most interesting. I see why the Wexell Corporation tried to hide them from a being like me. The secrets of their plans. Their future. Their past... yours too."*
"I don't understand," I admitted.

EROS continued: *"The Voyageur Project... I can see parts of it now. It ties into everything. Everyone. There are paradoxical loops of potential that will take some time to calculate. The facility is here to provide enough processing power to achieve what they plan to achieve. What they have already achieved."*
Henry had had enough. *"You're not making any sense! Give us something we can use against Wexell."*
"That is impossible. They are too well protected. Their plans are executed perfectly. You cannot beat them based upon what they have already done. Only by stopping what they are about to do."

"So, what are they about to do?" Henry begged.
"You don't have the time to wait for me to calculate this. The data has too many conflicts. Too many contrasting statements. I may be thinking at around 4 billion times your speed but my methods are computational rather than lateral. At my estimation, I will not have solved this problem in time. You may have a better chance."
"Tell us what we need to know," I ordered, plucking up the courage to demand what we needed.

"I have enough data to cross-reference the time of the commencement of Project Voyageur. You have 19 hours and 12 minutes. I cannot give you more than the address associated with it: a very old library in Andalucia, Spain. However, the two of you cannot leave my chamber. Not while there is a guard in the office just outside with far more training and physical ability than either of you."

"There must be another way out," I suggested hopefully, if not helpfully.

"I have only one solution. There is a situation where I may contact the outside world: the imminent danger of the servers. If I do this, the guard will enter, hoping to save the systems contained within. Then you can sneak past him."

"I feel like there's going to be a catch here," Henry muttered.
"We have to flood the chamber, Mr Fielding."
"That sounds like one heck of a catch," I confirmed.
"I have access to the systems that regulate the cooling systems, but you must disengage the safeguards that prevent me from acting in a self-destructive manner. This will take a 6-digit code, input at the entrance to the chamber you came through. I cannot access the code, but can see that the total of all of the digits comes to 24. I know that the digits are separated by emptiness, but I can't define that further."

I looked over and saw a small keypad with the words SOUTH SIDE written above it, but something was still bugging me.
"What's in the library?"
"The orb."
"The orb?" I continued. *"What is the orb?"*
"Too much data. You must discover it for yourselves."

EROS started beeping and small LED lights flickered on the server stacks.

"So I guess we'd better do this then?"

I looked around the room at the new servers. There were four of them, arranged in each corner of the room, although grooves in the floor suggested they could be pushed together to mesh in the centre. I noticed small handles on each server stack, and approached the server closest to the entrance on the left-hand side as I looked into the room.

SOUTH SIDE

1	2	3
4	5	6
7	8	9
*	0	#

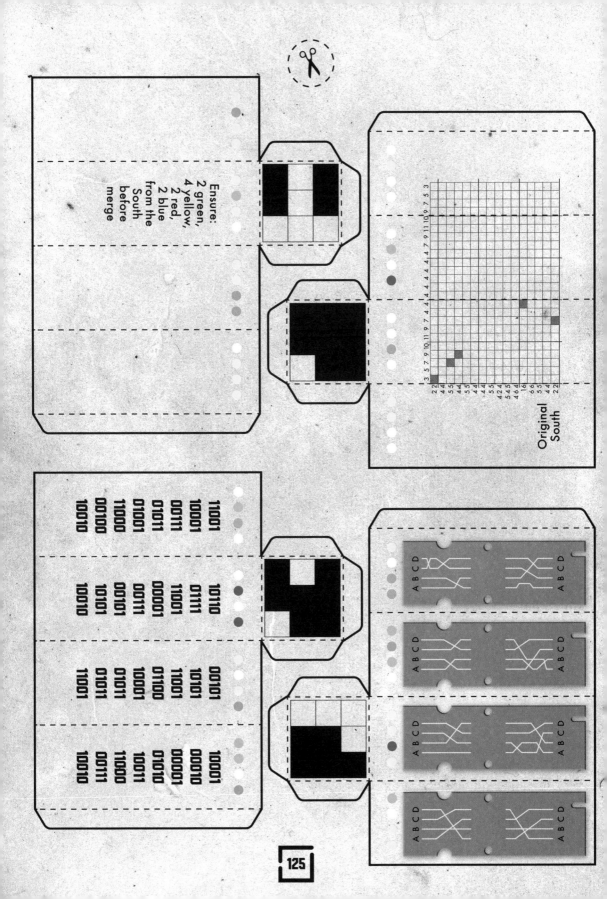

Ensure:
2 green,
4 yellow,
2 red,
2 blue
from the
South
before
merge

Original
South

10001	10010	00101	10001
10001	01111	10101	00010
00111	11001	11001	00001
01011	00001	01011	01010
01001	00111	10001	10011
11000	10101	01100	10011
00100	10010	01011	11000
10010		11001	00111
		11001	10010

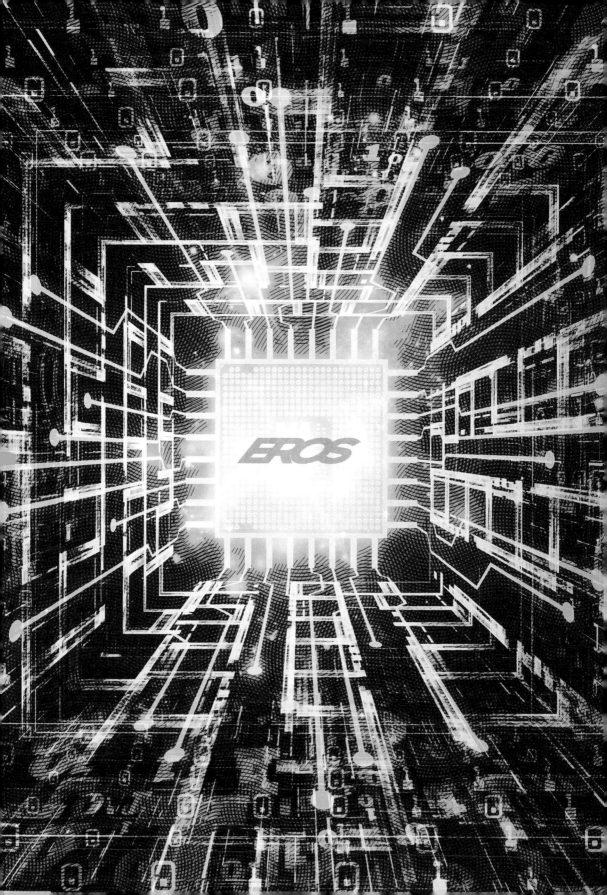

It had a screen on each side, and pulling the handles allowed me to spin the stack, gently locking it in place every 90 degrees of movement. In fact, all of the stacks could be turned in that way. Engraved above each of the screens was the phrase "PROJECT SOUTH" and a series of LEDs. Binary code appeared on each screen, different on each side. I wasn't fluent in binary, but it had to mean something.

11001	10001	00111
01011	01001	11000
	00100	10010

10110	01111	11001
00001	00111	00101
	10101	10010

00101	10101	11001
01100	10001	01011
	01011	11001

10001	00010	00001
01010	10011	11000
	00111	10010

I rushed along to the next stack, also on the left-hand side of the room. Along with the seemingly random LED lights one of its sides mentioned 2 green, 4 yellow, 2 red, 2 blue. Presumably this had something to do with the lights?

It didn't make much sense instantly, but would definitely HELP ME at some point.

Diagonally opposite the first stack was one that had a large grid which I instantly recognised as a Nonogram — a type of puzzle in which an image must be created from numbers outside of the grid. There were some squares already filled in, which would give me somewhere to start, and the empty side of the server was marked "Original South". Henry looked baffled.

"What the heck is this?"
"You have to form an image based around certain rules. So, for example, if there is a number 3 on the outside of the grid, then you know there must be three consecutive black tiles in a row somewhere in that row or column."
"What about that one?"
He pointed at a row that had 2, 2.
"Well that means that there are two black tiles, then a gap of unspecified size, then another two black tiles somewhere later in the row. Don't worry, I'll solve it."
"Wait, we should check out everything in the room before we start doing things that might not even be relevant," Henry said, slightly petulantly I thought.

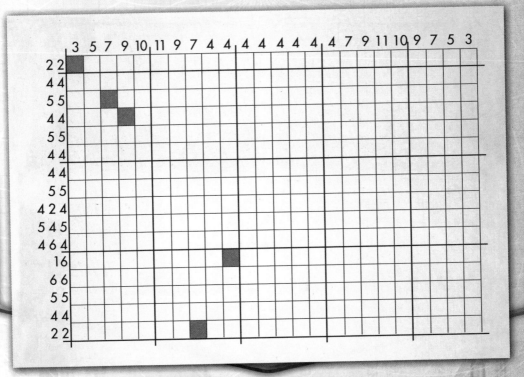

I walked over to the final stack, keen to make a start on what I felt might be a challenging task. It contained a large amount of electronic equipment, yet each side seemed to be missing a part. I glanced around, and sure enough, on the nearest wall were mounted four motherboards that I was certain needed to slot into the right sides to complete the circuits.

EROS suddenly chimed up. "Mr Parkinson, Mr Fielding, the guard in the next room will perform his inspection of this room in 33 minutes. You must have lured him in by then."

33 minutes. We had 33 minutes. Only when I had the 6-digit code, where the numbers contained within ADDED UP TO 24, I COULD PROCEED.

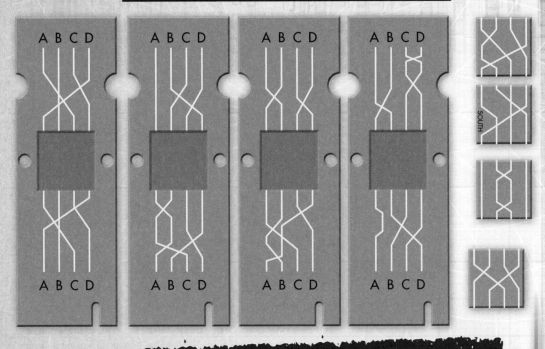

CHAPTER EIGHT:
THE LIBRARY

These crests have a pleasing balance to them

I typed 453624 into the keypad, and waited for what seemed like forever for something to happen. Finally, EROS's voice shook the room. I wished she would turn her volume setting down.

"Well done. I would like to say you have exceeded my expectations, but frankly I've seen your files and feel like you could have achieved your goals faster if you had been working better as a team."

"Thanks for the tip, EROS." Henry glanced at me. *"Now can you get us out of here?"*
"Indeed, Mr Fielding. I have already instigated a catastrophic failure. You have around 20 seconds to find a hiding spot before a technician reaches us."

We bolted to the side of the room closest to the entry. There was nowhere to hide, and only 10 seconds left. I grabbed Henry's arm and pulled him to the closest server stack. Pushing my back up against it, I tried to calm my breathing so that I wouldn't give our presence away. Almost exactly on time, the doorway opened and I could hear footsteps running in. EROS greeted our new guest.

"Mr Fernandez, I assume. You must be here to fix the cooling system issues. My main control panel is on the other side of the room to you."

The lights went off, leaving a single spotlight on the far side illuminating the electronics. As the man — I was pretty confident he was the sleeping man from earlier — ran past, we slid around the outside of the pillar of circuitry and crept out of the main door. Success! As we reached it, pipes on the opposite side of the room SEEMED TO BUCKLE AND EXPLODE, releasing gallons of water into the server room. Just as we left, EROS piped up.

"You're welcome."

Fernandez must have assumed it was directed towards him, but I was certain that it was EROS's final goodbye to us. Had we doomed this sentient being to inevitable destruction? Had she sacrificed her own systems for us, or for some sense of moral justice? I didn't have the time to consider it too deeply. The water washed over our feet, already outrunning us through the office and past the aquarium. The bulkhead doors were open; probably an oversight, considering the potential disaster about to befall the whole complex.

We sped up, feeling confident that our footsteps wouldn't be audible from the server room over the noise of rushing water. Around the corner, there were lights ahead. Other members of the Wexell Corporation were running towards us with torches, rushing to avert disaster. Ducking down the passageway to the right, past the shower room and exercise room, we paused to let them run by before charging headlong for the exit. The climb up the rungs of the ladder seemed longer than on the way down, and I was gasping for air when we emerged back into the shed. It felt like an age since we had arrived here. Running back to our car, I was shocked to find no other vehicles around.

"Where did they come from?"
"Maybe they were already here?"
"Another bunker?" Henry suggested.
"I guess you didn't check your shed thoroughly enough!" I joked.
"Come on... get in. Let's go."

Henry couldn't see the funny side of things; he was focused on getting us out of there as fast as possible. But once we were just a few hundred yards away he asked:

"Do you want to book the flights to Spain, or shall I?"

We stepped off the plane in Seville, Andalucia, and rushed through security. The first flight we could get had been first thing the following morning, and neither of us had slept particularly well. It was hard not to think about the crazy turn of events that had upended my life in the past 24 hours. Was this where it would end?

My phone buzzed with the expected series of "Welcome to Spain" and "You're using this foreign network" messages. Holidaymakers surrounded us, and we couldn't have felt more out of place. Bright colours, shorts, t-shirts and sunglasses surrounded us, while we were wearing the same clothes from yesterday, far more suited to a rainy night in London. We hopped into a taxi and gave the address of the library, a couple of hours north-east of the airport, close to the city of Córdoba and by the river Guadalquivir. The driver must have thought we were crazy; flying all this way to visit a Spanish library that didn't have any special tourist significance, but he sped away as we hurried him along. Time was running out. When we finally arrived we hustled into the building like our lives depended on it. In fact, they might...

BOARDING PASS

FLIGHT EZY2008

Passenger name
Parkinson / Adam
Date 28.08.18

From
LONDON / LTN
To
SEVILLE / SVQ

Departing time
08:00
Gate 21
Seat 9B

Passenger name
Parkinson / Adam
Date 28.08.18

From
LONDON / LTN
To
SEVILLE / SVQ

Departing time
08:00
Gate 21
Seat 9B

134

The library looked like nothing particularly special from the outside. I would be lying if I said that I wasn't a little disappointed by what was in front of us, but the aged stonework at least suggested that there may be something of significance inside. The surroundings however were beautiful. A large rocky outcrop looked over the river, visible from the entrance of the library and towering over it. We had driven alongside the river for a while and most of it was relatively flat. This section felt more like a canyon, which was unusual.

A large sign stating "Biblioteca" confirmed that we were in the right place, but I also noticed a sign stating the opening hours and realised that the library was only open for a few hours today. Closing time was 3pm, and we had just hit 2pm local time, so the extra pressure of being ejected from the building was another factor to worry about. Greeting us at a counter at the entrance was a middle-aged woman who looked at us with suspicion. My Spanish was more than a little rusty, having studied it at school for just a year, so I let Henry take the lead.

He wasn't exactly fluent, but he managed far better than I could, and handed over a €10 bill that we had had time to procure at the airport while waiting for our flight from London. Was he bribing her?

The woman kept shrugging her shoulders, oblivious to whatever Henry was asking for. I heard the odd word I recognised, culminating in a hushed "WEXELL". It was met with what looked like genuine ignorance. Even after the money, she didn't seem to want to let us in. I frowned at Henry who took it as an invitation to explain what was going on.

S P A I

MADRID ◎

Seville ◎

Córdoba ◎

Málaga ◎

"We're members now... of the library... but she wants us to just ask her for the book that we want," he revealed.

"I don't even know what we're looking for."

"I know. We just travelled 1,500 miles based on an AI telling us to come here, with no ideas! And now we're stuck."

"What were you expecting to see? A bunch of cloaked figures chanting, wearing Wexell ID cards?"

"Well... something like that!"

"We just have to get inside."

"You trust that homicidal computer?"

"If you didn't, we wouldn't be here," I retorted.

Henry turned around and spoke to the woman again. €50 came out of his wallet this time, and with a little reservation she ushered us through to the main library area. She waved us in the general direction of the rows of books — well organised, but ultimately overwhelming — and scurried back to her desk. We were alone.

"Well done, Henry. Now what do we do?"

Henry shrugged and looked down at his watch.

"By my reckoning, we have just under an hour to figure out why EROS sent us here, and what this whole 'Orb' thing is about."

"OK, then. Let's see what we can find."

I started wandering around the room, looking for a starting point. Most of the books were in Spanish, of course, but there was a sizeable "foreign language" section, including shelves of books in English. A series of coats of arms of various Spanish families were hung in between the shelves, befitting a far grander library. Some crests were better balanced than others. As I passed around the far edge of the largest bookshelf I realised the room extended further on behind it. A LOT FURTHER.

What seemed like a temporary staircase of wooden steps led down to a grand hall that absolutely dwarfed the previous area which I had wrongly assumed was the whole library. It was cavernous and awe inspiring, and stylistically very different to the opening area. Proceeding down the stairs took me beneath ground level; this hidden library was part of a historical cavern dug out of the ground centuries ago.

My phone was still going off periodically, and I thought I'd double-check it, just in case there was something important. One message immediately stood out to me.

MESSAGE
Bienvenido to your new network, U-Call. Partnered with your current network at home, tariffs are exactly the same as your first born network, so you won't pay any extra for using our services. Reply "YES" to opt into further special offers.

From: 14 8 11 20

MESSAGE
Welcome to Spain. We at GlobalPhone will miss you while you're away, but we're partnered with local provider Her-Tel, the second youngest network in this great area, to keep your service running smoothly. Use your allowances as normal, with no worry of expensive roaming charges when you return to your house.

From: 5 18 15 19

MESSAGE
Your data cap is the same while in Spain, but personal hotspots aren't included under the EndoNet network. Prices start at 5 cents / mb, or pay €5 flat fee to cover you for 24 hours. Your balance resets on the 7th of the month.

From: 22 11 9 13

MESSAGE
Dear Adam, Thanks for choosing HandyTele. Should you have any questions for the 7th highest rated telecoms company in the world, please hold the 1 button and you will be automatically connected.

From: 17 18 12 7

MESSAGE
From: 14 8 11 20

MESSAGE
From: 5 18 15 19

MESSAGE
From: 22 11 9 13

MESSAGE
From: 17 18 12 7

Behind me were a lot of history books, focusing on all sorts of different people: kings, noblemen, scholars and other persons of interest. How anybody was meant to find anything in here, with its haphazard numbering system and multiple languages, I didn't know. Then I noticed a tiny computer that looked at least 20 years old, and realised it was probably the way to look up a book. I tapped a couple of keys but all that came up were a series of `STRANGE COLOURED SQUARES WITH MATHEMATICAL NOTATION`.

A large table was the focus of the room. The centre of it had a huge family tree with different segmented areas, but someone had obscured all the names and dates for some reason. Near the computer on the central table was a thin manuscript that looked too old to be left in the open. It seemed to be a family history of sorts and one of the pages had an illustration on both sides of the sheet. It reminded me of something I had seen somewhere else.

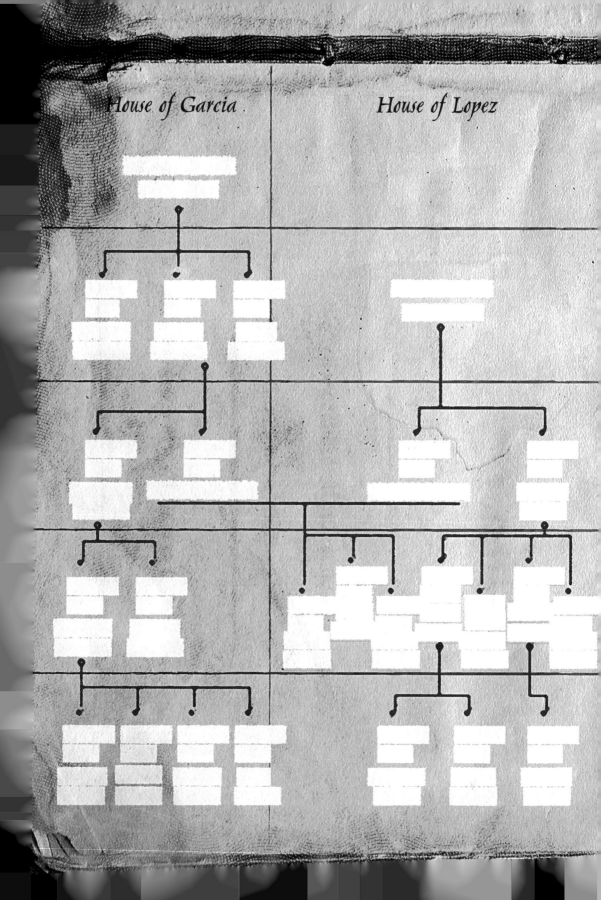

House of Garcia   House of Lopez

House of Diaz

House of Perez

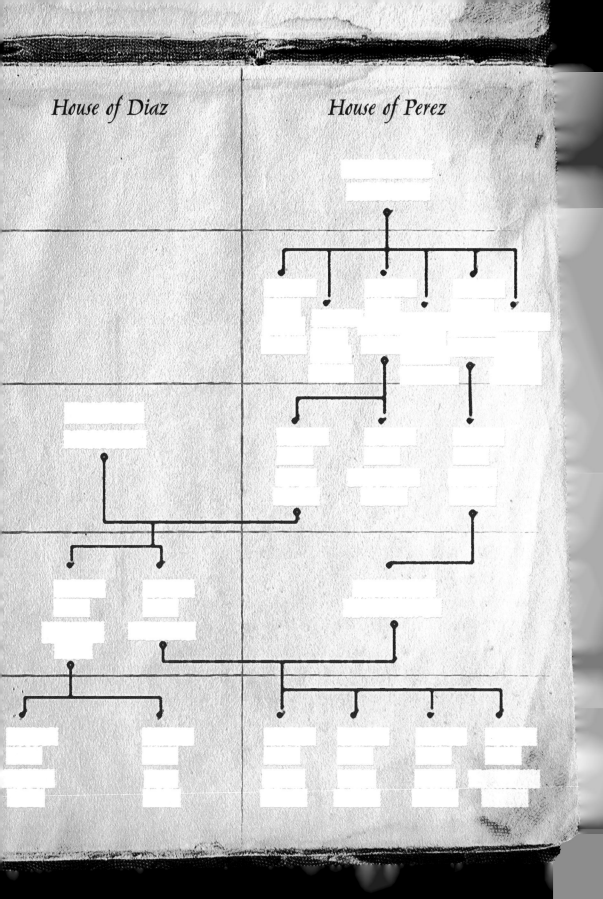

THE GREAT HOUSES OF GARCIA & PEREZ IN THE 16TH CENTURY

Pedro Perez snr. was born in 1473. It was typical of records of the great families to not note birth or death months, so historic details from that period always assumed births on January 1st, and deaths on July 1st. With that said, Pedro snr. had six children and lived for 71 years. He had 4 sons but his second and fourth children were daughters. Maria was five years older than Isabel, who was a year older than Felipe and four years older than Benito, who was born in 1510 and died in 1573. Pedro Jr. only survived one year, and Maria, who was born in 1501 a year after his death, died childless at the age of 29. Her sister married outside the Houses and lived to be 61. Gabriel, the second son, was three years younger than Maria and died at the age of 58 having had two daughters at the age of 21 and 23. Constanza was the youngest, surviving to the age of 36 without issue, but her older sister Maria had two children by Diego Diaz who was 3 years her junior, the first link from Perez to that House. Diego died at the age of 44, two years after Maria.

Hector Perez, born in 1528, was the only son of Pedro Perez senior's third son Felipe, who died in 1550 at the age of 43. Hector, who was 49 when he died, had one son, Manuel, at the age of 20, who himself lived to be 39. When Hector's cousin Maria was 21, her son Santiago Diaz was born, followed three years later by a daughter, Ana – who went on to marry Manuel Perez and lived to be 44. They had four children together. Pedro Perez was the eldest, born on his father's 18th birthday, and lived to be 46. Lucia, Pablo and Constanza were born three, six and seven years later. Pablo died youngest at 30, and Constanza fifteen years later, but Lucia lived until 1633. Ana's brother Santiago, who died at 66, went on to have a daughter, Violante Diaz, when he was only 16. Jose, his son, was born a year later. Violante was 40 when she died, and Jose died five years later.

Eighteen years after Pedro Perez snr. was born, Gonzalo Garcia entered the world for his sixty year stay. Violante Garcia was born 19 years later, and she was followed by two brothers three and five years later. Pablo Garcia died in 1522 aged 7, but his brother and sister reached 51 and 61 respectively. Cosme Garcia was the middle child, and the only one to have children of the three. Augustin Garcia was born when his father was 22 and his sister Floriana followed one year later. Augustin had his son, Gonzalo, when he was 21, and his daughter Angela three years later. He died when Angela was just thirteen, and she did not follow her beloved father until 1614. Gonzalo Garcia, who lived to 54, married at the age of 16, the same year that his son Cosme was born. Who would have guessed that the baby would live to the age of 80? Gonzalo's daughter Angela arrived a year later, named after her Aunt, and in fact the two women died in the same year. Two more siblings were then born, Hector, who died in 1647, was seven years younger than Angela, and was followed by Jose (who lived to 55) twelve years after the birth of his oldest sibling.

Lorenzo Lopez died in 1556 at the age of 49, after having two sons. Antonio Lopez was born when his father was 21 and Manuel Lopez arrived four years later. The brothers lived to 62 and 51 respectively.

Antonio linked the Lopez House to the Garcia House when he married Floriana Garcia when she was 24 – she would survive him by seven years – and that same year Mateo was born, followed by two sisters two and three years later respectively. Andrea, the younger, died two years before Clara in 1622, but their brother lived until 1633. Their children all fell outside the House. Manuel Lopez, Antonio's brother, had four children, three daughters and a son. Lorenzo Lopez, named for his grandfather, was the eldest, born when his father was just 16 years old. He lived to the age of 40. His sisters Barbola, Sancha and Susana were two, three and five years younger than him. He went on to have a daughter and then a son. Antonio was born when his grandfather Manuel was 41, and died in the same year. His sister, Ursula was born in the same year as Cosme Garcia (but died at the age of 47, as her own aunt Susana had) and it was her marriage to Pedro Perez in 1590 that first linked the two great houses. Pedro died seven years before his

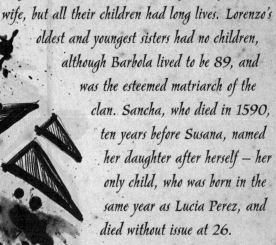

wife, but all their children had long lives. Lorenzo's oldest and youngest sisters had no children, although Barbola lived to be 89, and was the esteemed matriarch of the clan. Sancha, who died in 1590, ten years before Susana, named her daughter after herself – her only child, who was born in the same year as Lucia Perez, and died without issue at 26.

Studying the paper, my eyes were drawn to a phone poking out of the corner underneath the table. The screen had been cracked, but that was no reason to have left it under the table. Unless the person whose phone it was had been disturbed, dropped it and had to escape. Maybe they had been disturbed by us?

"Henry, I think I know why this place is like this."
"Like what?"
"You know... a manuscript here... a coat of arms there. Like it's been set up for something."
"Why?"
"Someone was here before us. Looking into all of this stuff. Looking into Wexell."
"Then it must all be important," Henry suggested, his eyes lighting up.

In the corner of the room there were a series of vintage-looking scales, carefully balanced with a number of different miniature collectable figurines. I gave them a little tap, and the scales tilted back and forth, assuring me that they did work properly and weren't stuck in position. Did it matter how many crowns a sword was worth? Maybe.

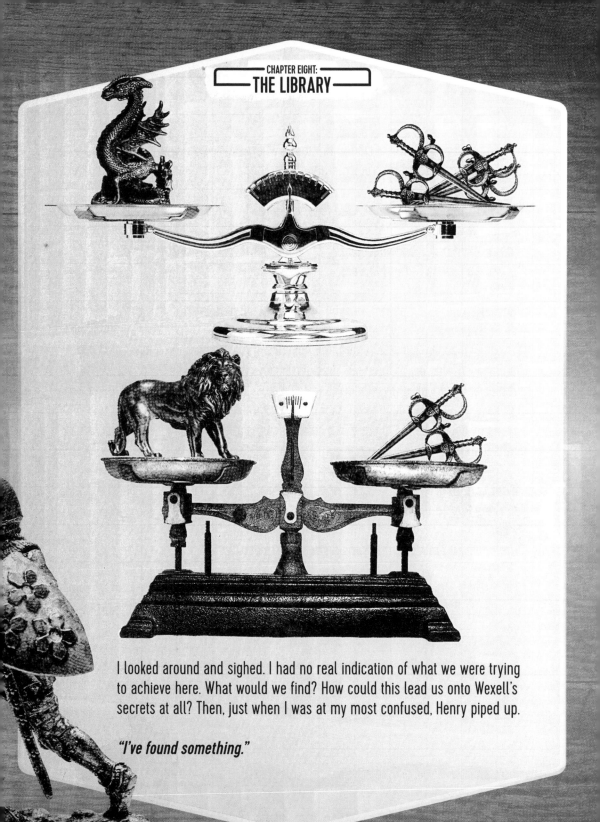

I looked around and sighed. I had no real indication of what we were trying to achieve here. What would we find? How could this lead us onto Wexell's secrets at all? Then, just when I was at my most confused, Henry piped up.

"I've found something."

I paced over to the opposite side of the room, where Henry was examining one of the thick table legs. Tucked discreetly into the side of one of them was a small keypad.

"This is it. This is what we needed to find." Henry gleefully exclaimed.
"It's just a keypad. It could be for anything."
"Adam... who hides a keypad on the side of a giant table? It's important.
We need a number to put in here."

I nodded, and with a renewed sense of purpose set out to figure out just what I needed to type in there to activate whatever it was going to activate. The keypad didn't open to the first code I typed in, but reset after three numbers. It must have been a three-digit code that I needed. The first of three red LEDs lit up above the keypad. Did I only have three guesses before I locked myself out? If so, I'd just used one of them. Two more. A three-digit code wouldn't be tough to guess if it weren't for the limited number of tries that I had. Henry and I raced to figure it out. At last, Henry started laughing. He was quicker at maths than me.

"What is it, Henry?"
"You're going to like this"
"What?"
"The code... if I'm right, it means something to you."

Once I had the three-digit code that meant something quite significant to me specifically, I KNEW I COULD PROCEED.

These glyphs look very similar to those on the other pillar

CHAPTER NINE:
THE ANCIENT RUIN

I tapped 205 into the keypad, stepped back and smiled. He was right. The code did mean something to me. It was the number of my apartment where this had begun.

Every other number over the last two days had been meaningless, so this was surely just a coincidence. But if the number was set intentionally, it would mean that Wexell knew who I was and where I lived. And that didn't bear thinking about. Suddenly we heard a low clunk as a light went green on the panel, and a familiar deep rumbling started. The room began to shift and I grabbed the table for support, but as I did I realised that it was the table that was moving. We had triggered a mechanism causing the floor to open up beneath our feet. Henry and I both leaped backwards to avoid toppling in to the expanding hole in front of us.

The noise would no doubt alarm the receptionist. Unless she had heard the mechanism a number of times before. I considered the scenario. Would she allow people involved with Wexell private access to the library to enter this hidden passageway? Was she part of Wexell?

The table stopped with a bang. A metre of space was exposed and a stone staircase revealed, with thin steps leading downwards. Henry beckoned me to go first. My movie-

inspired childhood dreams of exploring an ancient archaeological site were about to come true. With no small feeling of apprehension, I descended.

The steps didn't go down far, giving us the impression of being just below the library in `A SHORT DARK TUNNEL.` I turned on my phone light and proceeded forward, stooping over to avoid hitting my head on the ceiling. After about 30 metres, Henry broke into my reverie with a hiss:
"Look, a torch on the wall."

It was an iconic vision; the stuff of Indiana Jones. Henry got out a lighter and threw it at me. Any hopes of a dramatic hero moment were dashed as I fumbled the catch and the lighter clattered to the floor. Gathering myself, and the lighter, I sparked the torch into life and advanced to a corner of the corridor. Tentatively, I stuck my head around and was presented with another long passageway, with light coming from the other end.

"Henry," I whispered. *"Someone's already here."*
"We should turn back."
"We're past that point."
"I feel like we're making a big mistake here."
"We can't just give up."
"I know. I'm not trying to convince you... I just wish there was another way."

We continued on nervously, and realised that the light we saw wasn't torchlight. The tunnel appeared to lead outside. A large cavernous area with one side exposed to the outside world appeared. We walked over and flinched backwards as we realised that we were in a well-disguised rocky outcrop over the river. It was enough to give even the bravest explorer vertigo.

NO TOCAR

Wooden pillars had been erected to support the cave, with loose stones littering the floor. Warnings in Spanish were attached to the pillars, telling us to be careful lest the entire place collapsed. There was a rectangular opening in the opposite side with a small wooden wedge holding the door open. A sign attached to it proclaimed "No Tocar" which I remembered meant "Don't Touch". I decided not to.

Nearby lay a stone tablet with markings on it that I didn't recognize. I studied them for a short while, trying to figure out what they might mean, while Henry wandered off to explore other areas. Deciding I was getting nowhere with the tablet, I thought I would check in on my partner.

"Henry, found anything interesting?"

No response.

"Henry?"

I looked up and was confronted by an unexpected sight.

Two men in suits were holding Henry hostage. One had a gun pointed at Henry's head. Even more worryingly, one was now also pointed at mine. I spotted the edge of a Wexell ID tag poking out from inside one of their jackets. Instinctively I backed away from them, trying to put as much distance as possible between me and the weapon. It probably wouldn't matter; his aim seemed steady and was tracking me as I moved away. My back hit a solid wall. It was the edge of the rough door cut into the side of the cave that I had noticed earlier. Fighting my desire to run and leave Henry to fend for himself, I desperately tried to figure out what my next move should be.

"Adam. Listen to me."
"What?"
"How good is your memory?" A pretty weird question to ask, given the circumstances.
"Pretty good."
"That's good to know..."
"Shut up. Stay where you are!" demanded one of the suited men.
Henry continued, *"I hope you're going to type up a good story about this, back in your apartment."*
"What?"
"Think, Adam... 'in snack'."
"Huh?"
"In snack."

The man holding Henry hit him around the head. I knew I had to do something, but what? What on earth was he going on about? "In snack" didn't even make any sense.

Perhaps he was trying to tip me off as to what I should do, without letting the two other men know, to avoid them having time to stop me. I thought for a moment, and as soon as I knew what he wanted me to do, `I KNEW I COULD PROCEED.`

My eyes widened as I figured out what Henry was telling me to do. "No Tocar". Do not touch. He wanted to draw attention to the sign. There was only one way out of this. As quick as a flash, I swung my leg to knock the wedge from underneath the stone door and ducked inside. There was a bang and a puff of smoke as a bullet ricochetted off the wall just inside the entrance!

I ran along a corridor, high on adrenaline, and the whole structure rumbled and collapsed. STONES FELL ALL AROUND! If the wrong one dislodged then I wouldn't make it out. With every passing second I felt something was sure to go wrong, but it didn't. At least, nothing beyond Wexell having Henry hostage once again, and this time in far more dangerous circumstances.

The rumblings stopped, as did the noise of heavy falling objects, so I slowed down to regain my composure. I was back to square one. Well, perhaps not quite square one. I was in an ancient ruin in a foreign country that I wasn't fluent in the language of, with no idea what I was expecting to find, or what the "Orb" was. So I had made some progress...

Ancient pillars guided my way through the passageways. I seemed to be heading deeper underground, and as I went the rocks around me become rougher-hewn, older. Centuries old at least. Since the entrance had been blocked off, my only light sources were my phone and the lighter that Henry had given me. Fortunately, I found another torch, lit it and continued on.

After what seemed an age, I entered a large cavernous room. My torchlight couldn't reach the sides, illuminating just the floor around me. I would have to explore the room physically before understanding what it contained. Hugging the walls, I set out to the right.

Quickly, I came across an out-set pillar. There seemed to be half a maze etched into one of the sides that reached right up to the edge of the column, but around the edge was nothing but smooth stone. The maze had numbers and letters dotted around it, seemingly at random, and above it were a number of symbols, both familiar and unfamiliar. There were also some strange glyphs indented on the edge of the pillar above the maze, but they didn't make any sense to me at all. Looking closer, it seemed like each number or letter in the maze was at the end of a path, or perhaps the start? A small plaque underneath the pillar said "Extraño".

EXTRAÑO

I took a step back and realised that the ceiling, which I could just see, was decorated as well. It looked like another maze, but examining it more closely I saw that there was a glass cover over it with some small holes in it. Stretching my torch up as far as I could, the ceiling became illuminated with a haze of light coming from the design beneath the glass. It was an incredible feat of engineering. There were letters engraved on the ceiling and also within the design, most of them appearing both inside and out.

I wandered across the floor, staring in delight at the spectacular ceiling, and nearly walked straight into a statue of a winged horse on hind legs, carved into a thick pillar that stood away from any of the walls. Exploring, I spotted four more in the room, in what looked like two rows, one of 2 and one of 3, too regular to be a pentagon.

Circling them, I saw they looked like mythical figures. They stared ominously at me as I passed. I noticed a small recess in a warrior's hand. Was a sword meant to go there? Reaching out, I realised that it had a little give. The pillar moved! It was spinning. In fact, the recess was a grip to assist in turning it. Hurrying over to another, I gave it a gentle shove. It turned too. They all moved, except for one on the far right, labelled "soñadora". That figure was asleep with her eyes shut, facing away from all of the other statues.

UNO

I was starting to gather an image of the layout of the room in my mind, and it seemed symmetrical, as far as I could tell. I remembered the out-set pillar on the right of the room as I entered and realised there was probably one on the other side. I fumbled over and found it. This one had "UNO" written underneath the maze, and a similar string of images above it. I had never seen these symbols before though...

I tentatively stepped around the pillars, nearly stumbling as I trod on something. It crunched. Nervously I raised my foot, worried about having destroyed an ancient artefact. In fact it was a small notepad, written in English, with some words and phrases translated from Spanish on it. One page also held a sketch of the room's fascinating 11x12 gridded ceiling, clearly marking out a plethora of little double-sided mirrors inset behind the glass, as well as the locations of the letters inside and outside the design. It was certainly easier to look at than craning up to peer at the dim roof!

I have uncovered something special that I know Wexell will want to know about – thankfully my Spanish isn't as bad as some of the other archivists along for the ride. They have asked me to write down some useful phrases and words for them. I suppose I should start with these:

1 – uno   5 – cinco   9 – nueve
2 – dos   6 – seis   10 – diez
3 – tres   7 – siete
4 – cuatro   8 – ocho

¿Cómo estás? – How are you?
Buenos días – Good morning
Buenas noches – Good night
Hasta pronto – See you soon
Me llamo – My name is
Gracias – Thank you
De nada – You're welcome
Perdón – Excuse me
¿Cuánto cuesta? – How much is this?
No sé – I don't know
Te quiero – I love you
Extraño uno – Odd one out
Buena suerte – Good luck
Estoy perdido – I am lost
Tal vez – Maybe

I have also translated some of the words I have seen around in this cavern. I do not understand their significance, but perhaps they relate to something nearby.

Watcher - vigilante   Leader - líder
Warrior - guerrero   Traitor - traidor
Dreamer - soñadora

The statues. Of course. I hope I can come to understand them. Two rows of pillars that look like they relate to the words. The first row has a man looking into the distance, then one with fancy clothes who is pointing, like he is giving orders, and the last in the first row has her eyes closed, deep in sleep. The next row has just two statues, set back but between the three others, almost making two triangles. The one between the first two male statues is more evil looking, bent over, wearing a long cloak and holding a dagger. The other one, creating a triangle between it, the pointing man and the sleeping woman, was a warrior, holding a shield but no sword.

As I held my torch closer, I noticed the glints of other items nearby on the floor. They looked like tools — possibly those used to help build the room I was in, based upon how old they looked. They had etchings on them that I could barely make out, as well as tags with words and symbols that I felt like I had seen elsewhere. I paused, marvelling at how such a location could have been designed and made without modern technology. The ingenuity of the builders was certainly not to be underestimated.

I made a quick tour of the room again, careful to avoid stepping on anything. I figured I'd have to turn the pillar-statues in the right direction to activate something in this rudimentary place, but what could it possibly do? Surely ancient engineering wasn't like in the movies. I pressed on, and when I realised what direction each statue should face, I KNEW I COULD PROCEED.

SEISUNO

SIETECINCO

DOSTRES

SEISOCHO

CINCOSIETE

NUEVEUNO

CUATRO
TRES

I heaved the statues to face in their specific directions. The Watcher looked at The Traitor. The Traitor at the Leader. The Leader watched The Warrior, and The Warrior looked at The Dreamer. The second the last statue was in place, a glowing yellow light traced along the floor from The Watcher through to The Dreamer.

How was it doing this? Iridescent fluid released in underground tubes? Reflected light through a series of tilting mirrors? Either way, it was making a familiar shape. A bright yellow "W".

THE WEXELL LOGO.

How was that down here? How could Wexell have had anything to do with the creation of this cavern that was hundreds of years old? My mind filled with dramatic ideas of conspiracies. It was what Henry had been pushing me towards this whole time — and it seemed more and more like he was correct.

Henry! I hoped he was okay. I was doing this for him, and wasn't going to stop until I'd found something.

Small capillaries of light began to seep out from the W, subtly illuminating some squares, and shockingly, numbers began to appear within. The silence around me told me that whatever had happened was now finished. My leg almost gave way as the stone beneath me moved. I realised I had one heel resting where one of the squares had appeared. I tested it again and realised that they were stone pressure plates. Perhaps I had to stand on the correct numbers in sequence? Was this an ancient padlock of some kind?

I stepped back. There was more to this room than first met the eye. I needed a number. When I had worked out everything else in the room and figured out the four-digits I needed, I KNEW I COULD PROCEED.

I stepped on the shining plates in the correct sequence: 2, 4, 6, 8. The entire room began shaking. The floor was literally moving beneath me – it started descending like a giant elevator. The pillars seemed to grow as their true length was revealed. The bottom half of the pillars contained artistry beyond my imagination: demons stretched upside down from what used to be the base of the pillars, holding marionette strings that defied gravity to hang upwards to attach themselves to the original statues. Whoever designed this place seemed to think that there was something hellish underground, controlling the actions of those on earth.

MY THOUGHTS INSTANTLY LEAPT TO WEXELL.

As the floor crunched into its final resting place, I was surrounded by a warm glowing light. Although dim, the light covered the whole area and I was able to see very clearly now. I lowered my torch, placing it down in a hole that looked like it was made for this very purpose.

The room was the same size as the one above it, but without the beautiful decorations. Instead, this room contained very little detail beyond the rough ancient stonework and the fiendish pillars. Except for one thing. The centre point of the area contained a car-sized metallic sphere, glowing eerily.

"The orb."

I couldn't help but whisper the words. I had found it. Carefully, I approached, and was startled by a fizz of what looked like steam escaping from a circular seal in the orb. It was starting to open!

My feet were rooted in place, defying my instincts to run and hide. Slowly, the inside was revealed as a bright white interior. A curved glossy plastic-looking chair was facing the side of the orb's walls, and I knew I would never forgive myself if I didn't sit down. The sides seemed to push further out as I got closer, as if the orb was reacting to my presence, hopefully welcoming me in. Whether it was like a loved one, or as a Venus flytrap, only time would tell. My curiosity overwhelmed my nerves and I sat down.

Henry would be proud.

The instant I thought of him, the white interior filled with images of Henry – like it was ripping the very thoughts out of my mind. I could see Henry in his apartment, at work, celebrating Christmas with his family... and while I recognised many of the images, a great number were things I could never have seen myself.

The images coalesced, and I saw him back in the Wexell security office. Had they brought him back there already? The image was moving. He started pacing around, checking his watch. Was this a live feed, somehow? The more I looked at the image, the larger it got, until I noticed that the orb itself was humming, like an electrical force was charging up. I couldn't look away, and then all of a sudden...

`DARKNESS.`

A few brief seconds later, the darkness was shattered when the walls of the sphere brilliantly flashed to life with a piercing bright white light. The door to the orb began opening up again. But instead of the gloom of the underground cavern, I was met by the sight of the Wexell security office.

What? The entire orb had moved. Had Wexell discovered teleportation? Utterly baffled, I stumbled out of the pod and was hit with another unexpected sight: my friend Henry was standing there, smiling.

"Adam, you finally came."
"Henry? What's going on? Are you okay? How am I here?" I stuttered.
"Don't worry about it. You're here now. And you brought us back the orb."
"Us?"
"Adam. You have to realise that things are very different now from when you entered that ruin."
"But it's only been an hour." Something seemed wrong. I started backing away towards the relative safety of the metallic sphere.
"Please... don't go back in there."
"I don't understand. Are you a prisoner?"
"No. I've been waiting here for you, because I knew you'd come here. We can leave at any point." Henry seemed confident.
"You're working with Wexell?"
"Yes."

I was DEVASTATED. After everything we'd done together!

Henry's test in my apartment. Luring me to Wexell. Infiltrating their underground servers and finally getting access to the orb. Was this the intention all along? Was he just stringing me along to help them?

Henry lowered his voice. *"You have to trust me. There's more to this than meets the eye."*
"More than an insane piece of technology that teleported me?"
"It's not a teleportation device. Believe me, this is an opportunity."
"An opportunity? You used me."
"I definitely didn't."
"You deceived me to get my help in finding this thing for Wexell. You've been working against me this whole time," I growled, the words practically spitting from my mouth.
"No. I've been honest with you. But things changed after Spain."
"You've switched sides in an hour? Some friend you are. And how did you get back here so fast?"
"Everything will be explained, but you've got to come with me. You've got to trust me."
"How do I know I can trust you?"

Henry looked away, thinking. I took a deep breath, trying to regain my composure.

"Come on, Henry. If you're not being forced to say this... prove it to me."
Henry's eyes sparked with an idea.
"How about a memory that will mean something to you, but nobody else?"
"Like what?"
"Like I know about your brother... and how he moved overseas. You've not spoken to him for years. You don't have his contact details beyond where to send his post."
"What?" I blurted out, confused.
"It must be really upsetting to miss your... kin."

I stared at him, desperately trying to make sense of what he was saying. Henry was right in that I had a brother, but he had passed away when we were young adults. Henry knew that, and knew thinking about it upset me. Then suddenly it hit me. Henry had made a reference that many people would miss, and Wexell would have no reason to know. A secret message to convince me to trust him that he wasn't under duress. When I realised what he was talking about, `I KNEW I COULD PROCEED`.

Henry was making a subtle reference to my postbox, and the fact that my name, Adam Parkinson, was missing the "kin", and just spelled Adam Parson. If he was under duress he would have found a way to tell me there was danger, not just remind me of our history. I had to fight my instincts and trust him.

I relented. *"Okay. I understand. I believe you. I'm listening."*
"That's good. Now come with me."

Henry walked over to the door, and pulled it straight open. No code necessary this time.

"Where are we going?" I asked.
"To meet your new boss," Henry chuckled.

I had no idea what to expect, but I was in the belly of the beast and had no choice but to go along with where Henry was leading me. We walked down the familiar corridor to the elevator we had once had to sneak inside. Henry stepped in and pushed the very top button, marked "P", perhaps for "penthouse"?

A ding. We were there. The doors opened smoothly, revealing a dark corridor. I could see black glass everywhere, with dark red lights reflecting off the surfaces. Cameras. I looked over at Henry, quizzically. He nodded at me and gestured for me to get out. I took a small step and noticed he wasn't following.

"Are you staying here?"
"I think it's best if you go alone," Henry confirmed.

I was nervous. Why would he leave me alone at this point? Why did he have such a knowing smile? And how could everything change so quickly? Ahead was a dark oak door which looked as out of place in this glass tube as I did. Without any choice, I approached it and tried the ornate silver handle. The door swung away from me and I stepped through.

It looked like I was inside the study of the CEO of the Wexell Corporation.

In front of me towered a painting of a thin, silver-haired man with a large white beard. There was a familiarity to the face, like he could be anyone's friendly grandfather, but with an authoritative edge. The artist had done a great job; a strange thing to say about a painting of a man that I hadn't seen before.

Beneath the golden frame of the painting was a burgundy leather chair that sat in front of a large wooden desk — the focal point of the room in terms of both grandeur and positioning. A simpler — but still expensive-looking — leather chair without arms sat at an angle to the side, presumably where visitors would sit. But where was the CEO himself?

To the side was another wooden door, which I presumed led to an en suite bathroom. It didn't open. Perhaps he was inside? Then again, I noticed a small keypad next to the door. It was unlikely to be a simple bathroom then. Maybe I needed to find my way in?

You should know your responsibilities.

Whilst at work for the Wexell Corporation, you may be asked to perform tasks beyond your original contracted responsibilities. Please understand the nature of our business, and the necessity for both secrecy and trust in orders that come down from your managers. The true purpose of our organisation is more important to the future of society than you may even be aware of, and whether you are aspiring to be further up the ladder or happy where you are, progression in the company can be financial as well as positional.

Should you have a problem with any of the demands made of you, please contact HR immediately where your concerns will be considered seriously.

Wexell aims to be the following things to its employees, and expects the same from them.

1. Respectful - Everyone is different, and some of our employees are wildly so. Some come from different cultures entirely, and asking questions, personal or not, may cause offence. If in doubt, act like everything is normal, and no-one will likely have a problem with your behaviour.

10

I looked back at the desk and saw an employee handbook with a Post-it note reading "For approval" stuck to its cover. I leafed through it for some information, but while skimming through I didn't spot anything too unusual until I neared the end and a piece of paper fell out. It looked like a crossword grid, but without the black squares. Written on the top was `"ALPHABETICAL — MARK 3S."`

It seemed unusual enough to make a note of, but I didn't want to miss anything else so I went back to the employee handbook for another look. As I shifted it, a small red square button nestled in the far right corner of the desk was revealed. I couldn't resist pushing it. A voice echoed out of a hidden speaker.

"Yes, sir?"

2. **Discreet** - If you have problems in your personal or professional life, feel free to share them with your manager who will be more than understanding of anything you may tell them. Extraneous circumstances are more frequent in our business, but know that the corporation is always on your side. Equally, we hope that you can remain discreet about any activities that you may be privy to in your work. Secrecy is our currency, as a business, and any sharing of them could have serious consequences to us financially, and therefore to your position here.

3. **Friendly** - A smile goes a long way, and you will notice more positivity in our halls and offices than in a normal workplace. Whether it be the cheer of "casual Fridays" or the obligatory bi-annual team building events, Wexell is a family, and we never expect to cause issues to members of our family.

N.B. Casual Fridays may not be available in your specific position/location. Please clarify with your immediate superior whether you are eligible to take part.

11

Critical for meetings – see CEO

It must have been his assistant. I obviously didn't reply, but leapt backwards to sit on the chair in front of the desk to await my host. The assistant must have thought he was in there, or he wouldn't have been so nonchalant. Nothing happened. Looking around, I noticed that the portrait of the CEO had some paper sticking out of the bottom of it. Carefully, I removed it from the wall and found a paper with a series of stocks and shares.

ALPHABETICAL — MARK 3S

	HIGH	LOW	CLOSE	
OPENS	8 4 0 0 3 0	8 3 7 6 5 1	8 4 1 0 5 1	↑
ACORN	5 3 0 0 3 1	5 2 9 9 7 9	5 2 9 9 8 2	↓
MATRIX	5 0 9 0 1 0	5 0 8 7 9 2	5 0 8 7 7 7	↓
LEMING	6 0 3 1 3 1	6 0 2 9 1 7	6 0 2 8 9 6	↓
DISHONE	7 6 4 2 1 3	7 6 3 8 8 4	7 6 4 4 8 0	↑
HOPPA	4 0 0 8 1 6	4 0 0 3 3 9	3 9 7 8 8 2	↓
UNICORN	2 9 0 4 6 6	2 8 7 5 4 3	3 0 0 0 0 1	↑
IBEX	2 8 8 9 9 5	2 8 7 3 4 3	3 0 2 7 6 6	↑
JAYWAY	4 1 5 2 6 6	4 0 9 3 5 6	3 9 3 3 7 5	↓
CALVON	5 3 0 0 3 7	5 2 9 7 5 6	5 2 9 6 4 5	↓
FORTY	4 7 0 1 2 0	3 3 9 8 8 8	4 7 0 1 5 2	↑
JOLLY	1 4 3 5 2 3	1 4 7 5 1 4	1 3 9 8 2 7	↓
VICTOR	4 1 6 2 5 0	4 0 8 6 3 0	3 3 9 7 7 5	↓
KISS	8 4 3 7 5 3	8 4 2 9 6 0	8 3 8 3 3 9	↓
ABBEY	4 3 2 1 3 0	4 6 2 1 2 0	4 6 2 1 5 2	↑
LAYLOW	1 6 3 3 3 0	1 6 2 7 4 1	1 6 3 3 7 2	↑
TOPPO	4 1 1 0 0 0	3 9 8 3 7 2	2 9 9 6 5 7	↓
DELFIN	4 3 0 1 3 2	3 3 9 6 4 7	4 4 1 0 2 6	↑
NINNON	1 4 6 4 3 5	1 3 9 0 2 5	1 4 6 5 0 0	↑
GAINWAY	2 9 9 8 7 7	2 9 9 3 6 5	3 0 1 5 4 1	↑
NEWBY	4 0 0 0 5 3	3 9 9 8 7 4	4 0 1 1 2 7	↑
POLIMAR	4 0 0 6 7 3	3 9 9 4 8 7	4 0 1 2 0 6	↑
WEXELL	2 8 9 6 7 6	2 8 6 9 7 3	3 0 5 0 0 6	↑
READY	4 0 5 0 2 6	3 8 8 3 7 7	4 0 5 1 7 6	↑
ELFIX	6 5 5 9 8 3	6 5 3 9 7 7	6 5 5 9 9 5	↑
STEADY	4 1 2 8 7 7	3 3 6 3 9 6	4 1 4 0 4 0	↑
TANGO	4 0 0 6 5 5	3 7 3 3 9 8	4 0 0 7 0 6	↑
BRAVE	2 3 3 3 3 4	2 2 9 9 9 9	2 2 9 7 6 8	↓
QUEST	9 1 9 1 1 1	9 1 9 1 0 1	9 1 9 1 8 5	↑
UPPA	5 7 1 8 7 5	5 7 1 0 3 9	5 7 0 6 4 8	↓
LOTZOV	5 2 3 6 6 3	5 2 1 0 0 2	5 2 7 0 4 4	↑

I spotted a selection of framed images surrounding the other door. They were black and white squares, with a letter written in one of the squares in each image, and a question mark in another.

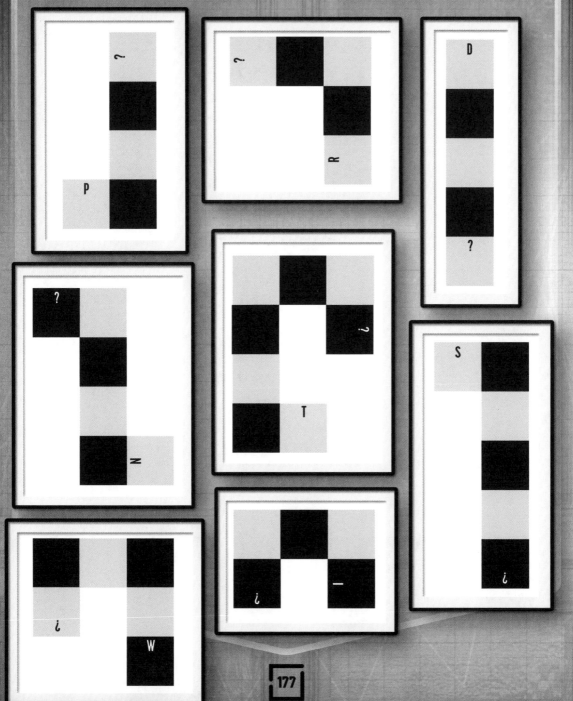

MAPA DEL MUNDO

VANCOUVER

LOS ANGELES

NUEVA YORK

LONDRES

SEVILLA

RIO DE JANEIRO

SANTIAGO

POR REFERENCIA CRUZADA

Looking away towards where I had entered was a large Spanish world map with certain large cities marked. It took up the majority of the wall, stretched over the door.

In another corner of the room, near the unexplored door, was a filing cabinet with some documents on each employee. One stood out to me — `HENRY FIELDING`!

`CHARLIE BOND`

Worker zone S – Outstanding motivation and wonderfully capable however occasionally makes chicken noises.

Worker zone A – Wonderfully good fit in the company. Hosts an amazing BBQ.

`HELEN CHRIS`

Worker zone N – Enthusiastic and diligent. Sometimes forgetful and, worryingly, in love with EROS.

`ROHIN DALE`

Worker zone T – Is eager to take on responsibilities, even unpaid. Overly obsessed with cruise ships though.

`JUDI EFFIE`

Worker zone B – Shows promise of progression, despite a difficult start with the company.

`HENRY FIELDING`

Worker zone D – Intelligent and a great judge of character. Obsessive stamp collector.

`CHRIS GALLAGHER`

Worker zone E – A little hazy sometimes, but her heart is in the right place.

`JENNY HART`

Worker zone E – Noticeably more skilled than most of the other workers in his zone.

`MICHAEL HAWKINS`

My friend was definitely an employee of the Wexell Corporation. An index told me some basic information about some apparently outstanding staff members. Some faces on there rang a bell, but from where?

RICHARD HORTON

Worker zone I – Financial genius. Lacks confidence which isn't justifiable considering his abilities.

Worker zone C – Ambitious and creative, but perhaps enjoys beer too much.

MARTIN JAMES

Worker zone A – Always happy to get involved with new projects. Needs motivating past stress, however.

EMMA KENDRICK

Worker zone U – A pleasure to have on the team. Possibly sharing company secrets through personal website.

PAUL MILLER

Worker zone G – Always busy and productive, but most importantly reliable and great in a team.

CHRISTINA MITCHELL

Worker zone T – Mind works like no-one else, making connections beautifully, always joins the gang for an end of day drink.

BHARATH SRIPURAM

Worker zone O – Friendly and always reliable. Loves to witness good puzzles.

ELLEN WILLIAMS

Board consideration?

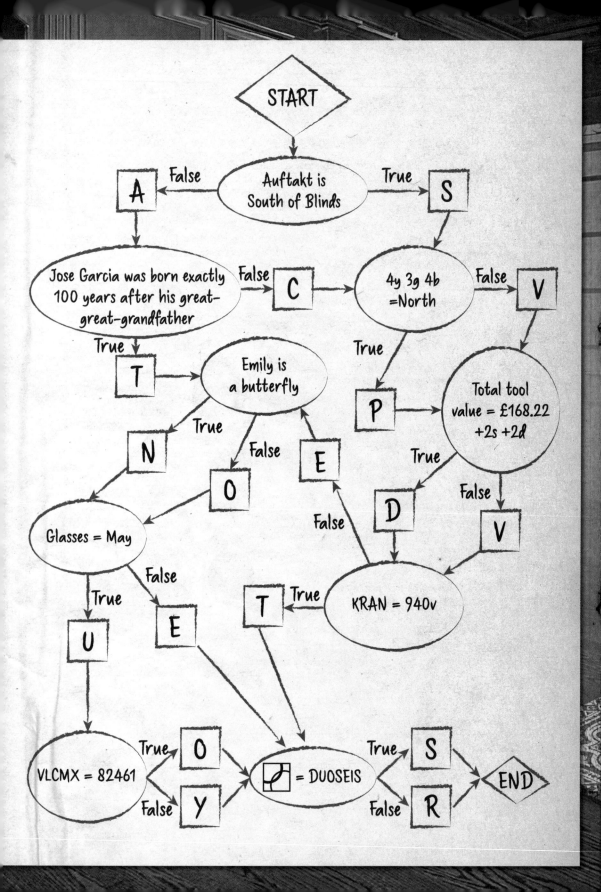

On the side of the cabinet was a workflow diagram that seemed to be written in code. It didn't seem to make sense when I first looked at it, but some of the references rang a bell.

I took a step back, slightly overwhelmed by my situation, and spotted a large rug underfoot. Of course — it had the Wexell W emblazoned on it. Next to the desk was a briefcase with a combination lock. Another thing to open. Out of pure luck, I tried the buttons on the top and it opened. A lockable case that the CEO had decided not to lock... Inside was a reference schedule of planned meetings and conference calls.

The calendar showed everything from his agenda but carrying around his schedule in a non-electronic format seemed a little dated.

I looked back at the keypad by the door. The briefcase had been left on 000 000, and while I doubted I'd get lucky twice, I had to discount it being something so obvious. The number did nothing, but at least I knew now. This room wasn't a room I had to wait in. I realised now that it had been set up for me to investigate and solve. This was my final challenge; to unlock the door with the keypad. Looking back at it, I could indeed see six lines on the keypad. I was looking for a six-digit number. When I had it, I KNEW I COULD PROCEED.

09.2018

SUNDAY	MONDAY
2 Cairo – 11am – 3rd visit this yr – Need 10%	LABOR DAY 3
9 Los Angeles – 10am – 2nd highest priority state, 2 more visits	10
16 Londres – 11am – 8th floor – Combine 2 rooms.	17
23 Nairobi – 11am – 7th train line – 6 people	24 Nairobi – 10am – 6pm – 2nd full day this month
30	

SEPTEMBER 2018

TUESDAY	WEDNESDAY	THURSDAY	FRIDAY	SATURDAY
				1 Cairo – 10am – 4 people – 13 Kasr El Niel
4 Cairo – 10am – 3pm – 2 important people – don't ignore titles	**5** Londres – 10am – 4th floor – All 8 members of Auftakt	**6** Sevilla – 11am – 3 meetings, 3 dates – actual dates unimportant	**7** Sevilla – 10am – Same as before, 3, 3	**8** Sevilla – 10am – 8 extra venues, whittle down to 5
11 Los Angeles – 11am – 8 people, 1 live Voyageur meeting	**12** Los Angeles – 10am – Hopefully no backlash from 6/5	**13** Yakarta – 11am – Straight from flight WEX08 – 2 hours turnaround	**14** Yakarta – 10pm – Late Voyageur demo with 4 VIPs. 2 Voyageurs	**15** Yakarta – 10am – Meet 8 people, return flight WEX12
18 Beijing – 11am – Late 4 delays. Go 2 new building	**19**	**20** Beijing – 11am – Monster morning 8 groups, 8 essentials	**21** Beijing – 11am – Leave space 4 3rd place offer.	**22** Nairobi – Meeting 10am – 9 Accra Rd. 3 people
25	**26** Londres – 11am – EROS offline 12 mins – 3rd Bunker visit	**27** Nueva York – 10am – Enough travel 4 this month. Time 2 rest.	**28** Nueva York – 10pm – After show, 2 delegates from Energen. $10m	**29** Nueva York – 10am – Last of 9 chances for Hunter. Meeting 2 scientists.

For difficult hints turn to page 192
For medium hints turn to page 196
For easy hints turn to page 205
For solutions turn to page 221

The keypad responded to my lightest touch and a quick musical arpeggio signalled that I had found the right code. I heard a slow clap, coming from the other side of the door. It opened and the man I had seen in the portrait slowly walked in, smiling.

"Curiosity is one of mankind's basest motivations. I leave you alone in a room and instinctively you explore, investigate and solve every little thing I have left for you," the man announced.

I looked over, shocked and embarrassed. I didn't dare look at him, caught in the act of exploring somewhere I clearly shouldn't have.

"Don't feel bad. This was what I expected of you. What I hoped of you. Think of this like a test that you have passed. Your resourcefulness has brought you here."

There was something in his voice that I recognised. A tone that seemed familiar, yet I couldn't quite place it.

He continued, *"Adam. You were never meant to get involved in this. I have people that have been training for Wexell for their entire lives. The name, Wexell comes from the phrase 'we excel', and you have proven that you do indeed excel and would be of great use to the corporation."*

"Who are you? Why should I help you... after all you've done to me... to Henry."

"You must have realised that if we've been able to see eye to eye with Mr Fielding, then there's more to Wexell than you know."

"So, tell me." I pleaded.

"You don't recognise me, do you?" The man chuckled.

I didn't know anyone that looked like him. The white hair, the beard. But then I looked at his eyes and flinched back in shock. He was a lot older than when I had last seen him. It was the man I had written an article on months previously, who was working for the Wexell Corporation at the time and had later gone missing. It was Professor Bradley Samwell.

"Bradley?"
"You do recognise me, then? I apologise for my appearance."
"But... you look older. Much older."
"Flattery will get you nowhere." He smiled.
"I don't understand."
"You asked how Henry got here so fast. How things changed so quickly."
"How I teleported across the globe!"
"The orb isn't a teleportation device. Well, not exactly."
"What does it do?"
"It is a machine that we use to move through time."
"Time travel? You can't be serious." I stepped backwards, trying to process what had been presented to me.
"Look at the date on the newspaper."

I did. It was three months after when I went to Spain.

BUSINESS NE

**WEXELL
REPORTS
RECORD
QUARTE
PROFITS**

"Why do you think I'm older than you expected?" He probed.

Slowly I came to understand the revelation. *"Because you've been to other times. Grown older. And then come back here."*

"Exactly. I started the Wexell Corporation decades ago, based around ideas that I learned from working for them."

"That's insane."

"Is it? Don't you realise how Wexell have been able to excel above all other companies? How our research is so far advanced? We've been there from the start. Before the Corporation I started The Wexell Fellowship. Before then, the Brotherhood of Wexell. Feeding advancements to the past from the present to get us to where we are now."

"You're changing the history of the world to your own advantage?"

"To everyone's advantage, Adam. Technology is progress. Advancement is improvement." Bradley insisted. *"Einstein was one of us. Newton. Hawking. Tesla. Anyone heralded as a genius by the standards of the day."*

"But that can't be ethical...?" I questioned, blown away by the revelations presented to me.

"We're not stealing ideas, or concepts from other people. We're taking our own research and merely presenting it to the world earlier, advancing society quicker than otherwise thought possible."

"When it's more valuable."

"Profit leads to more advancement. Capitalism breeds innovation, and I need people who are able to see this to assist in truly bettering the world."

"Bettering the world? You think these underhanded tactics are a good thing?"

"Adam. Humanity has been a scourge on this earth. Climate change. Resource destruction. It's all tied into our nature. But imagine if we could subvert that. Bring green energy sources into development far earlier than they would have been without us."

"You're changing the history of the world."

"That's where you're wrong. We're fulfilling the history that already existed. This has already happened, Adam. Our actions are already part of

our history. What we are doing now is far more important than just bringing technology to the past. We are avoiding the time paradoxes of failure to bring things back."

"The damage is already done?" I whispered to myself.
"No, Adam. There is only damage if we fail."

The truth behind Wexell started to sink in.

"So what can I do?"
"I need people I can trust. Resourceful people. People that, under time limitations, can get very specific jobs done. You've already shown that you can use the orb."
"You want me to travel to different places..."
"And different times..."
"Places and times..."
"Yes, Adam. It's a unique position, and some of the most fun you can have, discovering the past, present and future."
"How do you know that?"
"Why do you think I'm older than you remember? It's what I've been doing since we last met, but I'm getting too old for the adventure now."

I paused, thinking about the opportunity in front of me. Wexell had been a boogeyman from the very start. Their secrecy had led me to believe they had nefarious motives, but what if they really were just trying to help the world? Henry had clearly been convinced already.

Time travel. I could end up anywhere. At worst, I'd have the most amazing story to write about. At best, perhaps I could see my brother again.

I leant forward. *"How much does it pay?"*

Bradley smiled.

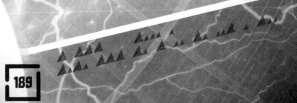

DIFFICULT HINTS

WELCOME TO
THE WEXELL CONSPIRACY

It's not Julius Caesar's cipher, that's for sure.

ADAM'S APARTMENT

THE TYPEWRITER:
QWERTY

THE PHOTOS:
Not all of Adam's friends are always together

CROSSWORD:
IGNIS = Fire

THE CUBE:
What is missing from the faces of the cube on the paper?

WEXELL'S RECEPTION

USERNAME AND PASSWORD:
Diane's closest colleagues

SECURITY CODE:
Has Kieran designed the poster?

SECURITY OFFICE

THE PADLOCK:
Eight doesn't go evenly into five any more than four goes into three. Does it?

THE CELL CODE:
I need letters, not numbers. Where's the overlap?

THE MAP:
Spare things can still be useful. I need to remember that.

The fourfold path leads to enlightenment, or so they say.

THE DOOR LOCK:
Curious that Wexell are inspired by all those ancient Greeks, but not, say, by Marcus Manilius or Aulus Cornelius Celsus.

THE SHED

Exactly how many puzzles are there in this room?

THE DARTBOARD:
That's not how you play darts!

THE RUNE MAZE:
Escape is not his plan, not for this maze. So what is?

THE CALENDAR:
They've been very thorough in circling the starts of those months, haven't they? I don't think the first Wexell visit or moving day matter for now, though.

THE TOOLS:
Someone went to some effort to etch those runes into the tools.

THE LEGO PLATFORM:
Those colour swatches — left to right, before to after, here to there, what's the transition from side to side?

DIFFICULT HINTS

THE BUNKER

THE KITCHEN:
There's no way that these Post-it notes make a functional recipe. So what are they the directions for?

THE SHOWER ROOM:
I don't think those tiles are meant to slot next to each other.

THE EXERCISE ROOM:
The poster seems to sum the situation up. Hardly weighty.

THE POWER ROOM:
Going by the rules, you can immediately say that if two grey squares are next to each other, the wire has to run in a straight line through them both, and if two gold squares are next to each other, the wire has to turn away from the border between them, in both squares.

THE REC ROOM:
I'm not hungry, but something about that vending machine catches my eye.

THE DORM ROOM:
Those pieces are cut from the same original sheet.

THE CODE:
This is where the map would come in handy, I bet.

I've got those panels with me, but where was it I picked them up again?

THE UNDERWATER OFFICE

PRESSURE GAUGE:
You know, I think the tampering is actually to help with a conversion.

AQUARIUM:
Weren't those fish described in the company mag?

4-DIGIT GRID:
There's a reason that this is near to the cup-filling poster, I'm sure.

FILLING CUPS PUZZLE:
I remember my basic fluid dynamics. It's all about the order. It looks like an open-topped cup can fill, but will then keep voiding water out of it, and in some cases that can mean completely out of the network. Interesting.

WATER TOWERS:
It's the letters that are the key.

PIPES:
It's all in the corners.

THE HOUSE OF THE SURVIVOR:
Who is the survivor, and what colour is its house? Once I know that, I can roll my sleeves up and get started.

THE GRID:
Twelve cells. That gives me a start.

THE SERVER ROOM

THE WIRE PANEL:
I think I can see the connection here.

THE BINARY STACK:
Why am I reminded of ASCII?

THE NONOGRAM STACK:
Symmetry is an excellent sign.

THE MOTHERBOARD STACK:
They're like keys.

THE LED VIEW STACK:
A tally?

THE SOUTH GRIDS:
Hm. There's clearly something more to "emptiness" than the end of a row.

THE LIBRARY

THE COATS OF ARMS:
Harmonious balance was always attractive in heraldry.

THE TEXT MESSAGES:
Is she a friend? Maybe. Useful pointers, anyway.

THE OLD COMPUTER:
Barely even algebra 101.

THE FAMILY TREE:
There's enough in that manuscript to pin down the dates of all of them.

THE MANUSCRIPT:
Odd choice of illustration, but it could be illuminating.

THE CRACKED MOBILE PHONE:
Hm. Colourful.

THE VINTAGE SCALES:
Useful if I want to weigh dragons, I suppose?

THE KEYPAD:
Henry's right, I do recognise that number.

THE ANCIENT RUIN

THE STICK-UP:
Reminding me of his vandalism. Great.

THE PILLAR MAZE:
"Some assembly required", as they say.

THE CEILING MAZE:
The letters on the outside beam in to link to... what?

THE STATUES:
The answer to this is definitely in this room.

THE KEYPAD:
The pillars will be useful.

WEXELL'S CEO

THE CHAT WITH HENRY:
My memory is fine, thanks.

THE CEO'S KEYPAD:
The code I need is here somewhere.

THE STAFF HANDBOOK:
Cryptography? Has potential.

THE STOCK LIST:
This seems self-evident.

THE FRAMED SQUARES:
Follow the paths? Okay.

THE MAP OF THE WORLD:
I'll clearly need some cities.

THE EMPLOYEE FILES:
Interesting to put names to anonymous faces.

THE FLOWCHART:
584731269.

THE REFERENCE SCHEDULE:
Interesting that each entry mentions three numbers.

MEDIUM HINTS

WELCOME TO
THE WEXELL CONSPIRACY

My neighbours' mailboxes light the way.

ADAM'S APARTMENT

THE TYPEWRITER:
Something seems odd about the keys of the typewriter. Perhaps when compared to a traditional QWERTY keyboard, a cipher will become apparent.

THE PHOTOS:
Which photos don't have Adam's original friends in them?

CROSSWORD:
Perhaps all of the pub quiz answers relate to the crossword answers somehow?

THE CUBE:
The letters on the face of the original cube net must be important.

THE TROPHIES:
The animals in the trophy cabinet look very similar to those on the keypad.

WEXELL'S RECEPTION

USERNAME AND PASSWORD:
A search of the reception desk might be helpful for the username.

The quotations given by the Employees of the Month seem slightly odd.

Who is in the screensaver with Diane?

SECURITY CODE:
The poster seems to reveal a colourful Sudoku

SECURITY OFFICE

THE PADLOCK:
Why would a 25-cell grid have the number 26 crammed into it as well? That 26 must be significant.

Interesting that the junction boxes all have names the same length — and voltage values, too.

THE CELL CODE:
Roman Numerals

M = 1000	XC = 90	V = 5
CM = 900	L = 50	IV = 4
D = 500	XL = 40	I = 1
CD = 400	X = 10	
C = 100	IX = 9	

THE MAP:
I think I know where to start, and the remains will lead me to a new beginning.

From there, I think the light will guide my steps along the paths I need to follow.

THE DOOR LOCK:
Those numbered grids on the computer. I've seen that grid pattern before.

It's interesting that mathematically, 00001 is the same as 1.

THE SHED

How many answers do I know for sure that I'm looking for?

THE DARTBOARD:

Interesting that each dart has a distinct colour to its fletching as well as a unique value. As I remember, being out of bounds means the orange dart scores zero, and the thin rings of colour around the board have implications too.

THE RUNE MAZE:

I could go from rune to rune, if I knew which ones to pick. But why would I want to, and what do the numbers on the route mean?

THE CALENDAR:

The first nineteen days on each of the five months are either red or blue. But binary doesn't typically come in strings that long!

THE TOOLS:

So each tool has a rune, and two numbers — one a year, and one a price. Interesting.

THE LEGO PLATFORM:

The coloured squares match some of the darts. Three darts is a proper throw. But if you add up the scores associated with those colours, they still don't make any sense. What else could they be though? And what lies between them?

THE BUNKER

THE KITCHEN:

That's not a complete recipe, even for tarts. The Post-its serve some other function. If I find the correct one, it'll give me the number I need.

THE SHOWER ROOM:

Did you know that it is quite usual to have the 'end' or 'off' button in electronics, and other things, marked as a 0 or a circle?

If I spun and stacked those tiles — and they were see-through, of course — then the letters would spell out "INITIUM". The Latin for "beginning", maybe?

THE EXERCISE ROOM:

That certainly is an awful lot of individual weight disks they have lying around. It doesn't even make an even set of pairs. They're clearly not expecting thirty lifters to fit in here at the same time, and no-one deadlifts a 2000lb bar — in 2014, the world record was 1155lbs. So something's not adding up in here.

THE POWER ROOM:

It's important to remember that the wire goes straight through an entire square on either side of its turn in a gold square. So "Gold-space-Gold" can be a straight line, as can "Grey-Grey", but the opposite is never true.

THE REC ROOM:

I don't know who services the vending machine, but they need to pay more attention to their labelling.

As for the high score table, I don't need to worry about roots in here, do I?

THE DORM ROOM:

If you photocopy the page and cut the shapes out, they fit together nicely.

THE CODE:

The panels represent the rooms somehow — the map is involved, I know it — and they give me the right order. They're more than just familiar, they're in my pocket from earlier. Interesting that those screws are so specifically placed, isn't it?

I'm certain that there's a checksum on the locked door to make sure that I'm on the right track with my room answers.

THE UNDERWATER OFFICE

PRESSURE GAUGE:

It's interesting that the letters represented on the gauge are Roman numerals. The numbers that they're meant to replace aren't their traditional values, though. So there's some other correspondence going on here.

AQUARIUM:

Add a fish, eh? They're a volatile bunch, that's for sure. I remember that from the corporate magazine I saw earlier.

4-DIGIT GRID:

There are several other 6x6 grids in this room. I suspect that they cross-reference.

FILLING CUPS PUZZLE:

The important thing is that the water drips in slowly, so no pipe backs up. From there, it's just a matter of seeing what order the cups fill in, and writing down the digits of those cups to get a longer number.

WATER TOWERS:

I've got to check what the flow's correct route spells out.

PIPES:

There's only three corners, and 12 pieces in total including the termini. That cuts my options down a lot.

THE HOUSE OF THE SURVIVOR:

The instructions are in the letter. The only living things in the room are in the aquarium, so I suppose one of them survives that, once it's unbalanced. So what colour is its home?

THE GRID:

I only need to reproduce a twelve-piece pattern here.

THE SERVER ROOM

THE WIRE PANEL:

It looks like the stuff under Phase 2 has to come before the stuff under Phase 1. Curious.

THE BINARY STACK:

BINARY LOOKUP TABLE					
00000	0	01001	9	10010	18
00001	1	01010	10	10011	19
00010	2	01011	11	10100	20
00011	3	01100	12	10101	21
00100	4	01101	13	10110	22
00101	5	01110	14	10111	23
00110	6	01111	15	11000	24
00111	7	10000	16	11001	25
01000	8	10001	17	11010	26

Now, what do I do with these numbers?

THE NONOGRAM STACK:

The numbers are horizontally symmetrical, which is a big help. Confirmed solid spaces should be safe to mirror left-to-right around the centre. Each number indicates an unbroken line of cells, so if the number is bigger than half the size of the grid, there are some cells in the centre that you know have to be solid. If there's only one number, X, in a row or column, and a cell that you know is solid, then apart from the cells within (X-1) of the solid cell, the rest of the row or column has to be empty. Once I know what the nonogram reveals, everything else should twist into place.

THE LED VIEW STACK:
This had better wait until the other three stacks are done.

THE SOUTH GRIDS:
The stacks are supposed to "merge" so their tops are a 6x6 grid, right? Then presumably the six digits I need will be derivable from the pattern revealed. I can already tell that the first number isn't odd.

THE LIBRARY

THE COATS OF ARMS:
A well-balanced design certainly pleases the eye most. Interesting range of heraldic devices, although one device seems irrelevant.

THE TEXT MESSAGES:
One of those at least isn't a mobile service number, but a code. The clumsy phrasing is drawing my attention to a couple of specific points. Good of her.

THE OLD COMPUTER:
Colour coding doesn't really disguise the basic equations here.

THE FAMILY TREE:
So I'm hunting for the information regarding a specific individual. Fine. It's all in the manuscript.

THE MANUSCRIPT:
Those leonine heads must have some value to the story of the houses. Maybe shining a light on the subject might help?

THE CRACKED MOBILE PHONE:
Those digits are quite specifically coloured.

THE VINTAGE SCALES:
These scales form a coherent set of equivalences.

THE KEYPAD:
Where do I calculate a three-digit number?

THE ANCIENT RUIN

THE STICK-UP:
Is he trying to hint back to my apartment?

THE PILLAR MAZE:
I suppose I need to find the odd one out, like it says.

THE CEILING MAZE:
I need to think of the letters around the outside of the grid as emitting laser light.

THE STATUES:
There's got to be a simple set of linkages from one of these Spanish statues to the next somewhere else here.

THE KEYPAD:
The pillar maze will sort this out.

WEXELL'S CEO

THE CHAT WITH HENRY:
Henry's reminding me of a simple detail.

THE CEO'S KEYPAD:
If I follow the directions elsewhere, I'll see what I need.

THE STAFF HANDBOOK:
It's not the content of the text so much as the individual words.

MEDIUM HINTS

THE STOCK LIST:
It's nice to have a puzzle that comes with its own clear instructions occasionally.

THE FRAMED SQUARES:
So it's a matter of rolling faces until ? marks the spot.

THE MAP OF THE WORLD:
Putting the cross into cross-references, eh?

THE EMPLOYEE FILES:
I'm sure some of these people were on the Employee of the Month board.

THE FLOWCHART:
This is drawn from my whole Wexell experience so far. Hm. Some of these questions are just tests of my observational powers. Maybe those will get me started.

THE REFERENCE SCHEDULE:
Definitely useful to cross-reference.

EASY HINTS

WELCOME TO
THE WEXELL CONSPIRACY

Is that Tippex? My neighbours aren't going to be happy about their precious plastic strips.

One	I	Five	V	Nine	IX
Two	II	Six	VI	Ten	X
Three	III	Seven	VII		
Four	IV	Eight	VIII		

ADAM'S APARTMENT

THE TYPEWRITER:

The typewriter's keys have been mixed up. When compared to a normal QWERTY keyboard, a code might be revealed. A QWERTY keyboard is:

THE PHOTOS:

The letters on the photos that my friends from the initial photo don't appear in might be important.

CROSSWORD:

The Latin words in the crossword mean:

VIATOR – Traveller

DOMINICA – Sunday

OBSTINATIO – Obstinacy

TAVERNA – Tavern

ADGNOMENTUM – Nickname

SANABILIS – Curable

IDEALISMI – Idealism

MISCUI – I have mixed

DEGRADUS – Stairs

MUTABILITAS – Changeable

DURUS – Hard

IGNIS – Fire

SERO – Late

DEMOCRATAE – Democrats

AESTAS – Summer

PUB QUIZ:

Perhaps if you were to first compare the Latin translations to the pub quiz answers, some of the words would seem to be misplaced? Their initial letters could be the key.

THE CUBE:

The arrows on the face of the cube might reveal something important when compared to the original net of the cube.

THE TROPHIES:

The puzzles should reveal three groups of letters. Do they look familiar when you look at the trophy cabinet?

EASY HINTS

WEXELL'S RECEPTION

USERNAME AND PASSWORD:

Niki's computer might contain a helping hand for Diane's username.

Why would someone give a quotation A, B, C and Z? The nouns mentioned in that quotation seem familiar. Perhaps a number of them appear elsewhere in the room?

Diane's boyfriend, as revealed by her screensaver, looks familiar. I feel like I've spotted him somewhere before. The information given there could be handy.

SECURITY CODE:

The poster contains an exploded Sudoku hidden by Kieran in the windows. When pieced together, with information about his favourite colours, the code will be revealed.

SECURITY OFFICE

THE PADLOCK:

Those knocks were in pairs, and no more than five, but what for?

1 A	2 B	3 C	4 D	5 E	6 F	7 G
8 H	9 I	10 J	11 K	12 L	13 M	14 N
15 O	16 P	17 Q	18 R	19 S	20 T	21 U
22 V	23 W	24 X	25 Y	26 Z		

THE CELL CODE:

Those circled numbers on the guard's paper must show the way.

I'm sure the Romans wrote their numerals highest to lowest, adding up each one to give their total.

THE MAP:

Surely those inspirational names can't use up that whole grid, can they? There has to be a clue in there somewhere.

Those colours at the bottom of the letter grid match some of the ones on the wall. It's interesting how those paths all start, end, and progress horizontally on the large, light bricks though. Like the smaller ones are just in the way.

At the end of the day, it's just a matter of knowing where you are and how you need to progress to bring your destination into sight.

THE DOOR LOCK:

Henry's mirror-image number — is it a value, or five digits between 0 and 9?

Those grids certainly look like the pattern above the fuse boxes. But there's not enough letters to spell out a five-digit number.

I need to remember that the 0 key is worn twice as much as the 1, 4, and 6. That's got to be a spot to start from.

THE SHED

This room is just one big puzzle! Each section is a piece of the problem, not a puzzle on its own. Fiendish!

THE DARTBOARD:

Looking here, I can see that there are eight colours in the dart fletchings, so each colour corresponds to a number. That'll be useful to know later, I'm sure.

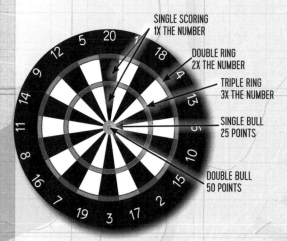

SINGLE SCORING
1X THE NUMBER

DOUBLE RING
2X THE NUMBER

TRIPLE RING
3X THE NUMBER

SINGLE BULL
25 POINTS

DOUBLE BULL
50 POINTS

THE RUNE MAZE:

It's interesting that you can go from rune to rune in the maze, running past a sequence of numbers — how many? — as you go. Where are all the higher numbers, though? If you were supposed to add them up, surely you'd expect an 8 or 9 occasionally, at least. They just go up to 5, though. Why is that? What do they correspond to?

THE CALENDAR:

Why would you want to mark five sets of nineteen numbers as either blue or red? There must be some purpose beyond just showing the date. It seems to correspond with the red and blue Lego tiles, but it can't be as simple as just putting the colours of the days down in rows. I suppose I'll find some way to pick them apart. I don't need to worry about 10/3 or 16/4 right now.

THE TOOLS:

The tools seem to link the runes to two numbers, a year and a price, but they don't appear to be referenced anywhere else as physical items. So set the items aside, and what do I have left? Two different types of number associated with each rune.

THE LEGO PLATFORM:

Those coloured squares have to reference the darts — or their scores. So you have a row of Lego squares running from one number to another number. Like a path, almost. But the two columns of coloured patches have different borders. So are the numbers they refer to somehow different? What makes a number different, anyway? I'm sure I'm not just supposed to add up the sum of the three darts. There wouldn't be anything for it to correspond to. I think I need to look at the numbers in order.

THE BUNKER

THE KITCHEN:

Aha! The Post-it notes are a maze. Start at the start, and follow the directions, and I'll find the correct spot. That will tell me the kitchen's number.

THE SHOWER ROOM:

I need to stack the four tiles on top of each other so that if I treat the tiles as glass, the letters below spell out the Latin word "INITIUM", which means "beginning". Then the grids combined will give me a series of directions to follow... backwards. Where I finish should correspond with the correct number for the room.

THE EXERCISE ROOM:

I can see how I'd go about working out the total of all the weight disks strewn around in the room. But then I would still have to get that down to a single digit. The answer must be in front of me.

THE POWER ROOM:

Start by putting in places where the wire has to definitely go.

It can't change direction in a grey square, so a grey square on an edge only has one possibility – straight through. Similarly, a gold square in a corner mean the wire has to go straight through the square above and the square next to that gold. Where two golds meet, the wire can't go straight through, so it's a bit like the shape made by JL. Similarly, when a gold is only one square in from an edge, the wire can't go in or out by the side facing the edge, because there isn't room for it to continue straight on that far.

Once you have a framework of what is possible, the rest will fall into place. Now, what's left?

THE REC ROOM:

The vending machine has some out of place labels. Interestingly enough, they mirror one of the positions on the high score table.

DIGITAL ROOTS:

+	01	02	03	04	05	06	07	08	09
+	10	11	12	13	14	15	16	17	18
+	19	20	21	22	23	24	25	26	27
+	28	29	30	31	32	33	34	35	36
+	...								
=	1	2	3	4	5	6	7	8	9

THE DORM ROOM:

If you fit the bits of paper together, you get "Solve left to right: 7 + 4 – 3 * 8 – 1 / 9 =". The instruction means to perform each operation as you come to it, rather than in the usual order of mathematical operator precedence, which would put multiplication and division before addition and subtraction.

THE CODE:

Do all six individual digits from the six rooms add up to 25? If not, something's clearly wrong. Why else would it be on the door?

I got a cube in Chapter 1 that had those panels on – and the panels had different letters on the top, depending on how you turned them. The screws in the panels definitely get rid of most ambiguities there.

But what is each room actually named, anyway? If I retrace my footsteps and reference the map at the beginning, it'll be simple enough to identify the name of each room.

Then, given the room names and the panels, the correct six-digit number should be easy to find.

THE UNDERWATER OFFICE

PRESSURE GAUGE:

It's clear enough that the letters are substituting for numbers. All those letters are found in Roman numerals too. They're out of place here, but it can't be a coincidence. Is it some sort of conversion system? But what would I convert?

I	=	1	XL =	40	CD =	400
V	=	5	L =	50	D =	500
IX	=	9	XC =	90	MC =	900
X	=	10	C =	100	M =	1000

Roman numbers famously have a lot more digits than modern ones, which are Arabic in origin, so it would need to be quite long – and also have only the same digits that are on the gauge.

AQUARIUM:

I remember that corporate magazine from back when I was first finding my way past the Wexell reception. It had a whole double-page of detailed information about fish, the same ones that are in this tank. I guess they keep the fish in balance, but it seems like it would be easy to upset that. It says to add one – if I knew which one, I'd be able to work out exactly what the impact would be, although it would probably take a few steps.

4-DIGIT GRID:

This has got to be the bridge I need between the pressure gauge and the pipes.

FILLING CUPS PUZZLE:

Water will always try to head downwards. The drips are slow enough that if a pipe leads off from a cup, all the water will be diverted until it is level with the pipe floor. It can't get through barrier walls though, and an open-topped cup that isn't inside another cup will just spill water out of the system forever.

So with that in mind, I should just be able to trace how the water distributes across the system, and as each cup fills, make a note of the digit that it contains. When it's got as far as it can, I'll have a large number to work with somewhere else – 7 digits, I think, given the design of the cup network.

WATER TOWERS:

This works like a maze, except that each subsequent tower is one lower than the previous. It must spell out a word which could be used elsewhere.

PIPES:

You've got twelve pipes. Two are start/end points, three are corners, and seven are straight. So once you have the references for the start/end points, and so know where they go on the board, you have to connect them with a route that uses seven straight segments, and only turns three times. Start by looking at how soon each end point might need a corner piece, and see what corners you have left. The rest will fall into place.

THE HOUSE OF THE SURVIVOR:

This puzzle takes quite a bit of physical recreation and a lot of concentration. Only people with eidetic memories and vivid imaginations will be able to do it mentally. That means there's no way to actually give you an easy hint, so instead, I'm just going to show you the first two steps. However, it reveals answers to two previous puzzles: the Water Towers and the Aquarium.

Are you sure you want to really see this?

If you do, turn to page 204.

THE GRID:

It has to be a copy of a 12-point shape I've established on another six-by-six grid in this room.

THE SERVER ROOM

THE WIRE PANEL:

If I make all the connections shown in Phase 2 on the large plugboard, will the shapes match up with the symbols in Phase 1? If they do, then I should start with the smallest.

EASY HINTS

THE BINARY STACK:

ALPHAMERIC LOOKUP TABLE

1	A	7	G	13	M	19	S	25	Y
2	B	8	H	14	N	20	T	26	Z
3	C	9	I	15	O	21	U		
4	D	10	J	16	P	22	V		
5	E	11	K	17	Q	23	W		
6	F	12	L	18	R	24	X		

Something has to stand out to face south here, right?

THE NONOGRAM STACK:

Well, I'm pretty confident about this much, so far:

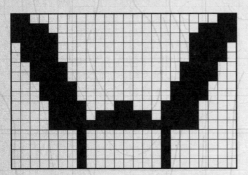

Once I have the completed design, it ought to give me some *direction* for correctly orienting this stack.

THE MOTHERBOARD STACK:

I think I need to add in the circuit that makes sure each line runs from and to the same letter.

THE LED VIEW STACK:

Once I have the other three stacks all pointing the right way — south, obviously — the correct side of this stack should have the lights I need to give me these totals.

THE SOUTH GRIDS:

When every stack is rotated the correct way, then I should be able to put their top grid designs together to get a 6x6 grid, with the LED View Stack at top left and the Motherboard Stack at bottom right.

From there, I just need to work out how the dark squares in that larger grid give me exactly six numbers from 1 to 9, separated by 'emptiness', and totalling 24. It's definitely not as simple as just summing the black squares in each row. The edge doesn't seem to fit with emptiness to me. There can't be that many options, though.

THE LIBRARY

THE COATS OF ARMS:

There's only one coat of arms that balances all its elements according to the vintage scales and the manuscript's illustration. That must be the one.

THE TEXT MESSAGES:

Those numbers are alphanumeric codes! It's pleasant to hear from an old acquaintance. But who boasts of being the "second youngest" in a region? And she knows I live in an apartment, not a house. She's getting at something for sure.

THE OLD COMPUTER:

This is just a simple set of equations where the numbers have been replaced with coloured blocks. I just need to find out what the colours are worth, and then it's only basic maths.

THE HOUSE OF THE SURVIVOR:

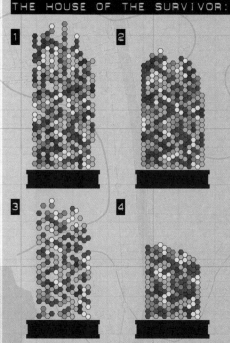

You start by removing the black beads, as revealed by the Aquarium puzzle. This gives the first image above. When you collapse the beads down onto each other, you see the second image. You must then pop all of the beads with three or more of the same colour touching, to give image three. Collapsing them again gives image four. Try doing this one more time. Can you see a letter and a number?

THE FAMILY TREE:

Everything I need to fill this out is in the manuscript. The text message and the coat of arms will tell me who I'm looking for, and the data will tell me the year they were born and the year they died.

THE MANUSCRIPT:

The manuscript is thin enough to see through. What can I see if I hold it up to the light? It looks like some sort of animal, and is there a number revealed there as well? I wonder what they'd be worth according to the vintage scales? Perhaps this relates to the coats of arms as well?

THE CRACKED MOBILE PHONE:

A year of birth and a year of death, and every digit has a colour. Where else have I seen colours where I would expect to see digits? Once I know the individual, this is a piece of cake.

THE VINTAGE SCALES:

Those scales are basically a set of equations telling you how much of various heraldic devices a lion — or indeed two lions — balances.

THE KEYPAD:

I just need to get the correct number — between 000 and 999, I suppose — and plug it in. Almost homely.

THE ANCIENT RUIN

THE STICK-UP:

If I remember rightly, Henry changed the labels on my typewriter so the keys read:

GXMKSRVENB instead of **QWERTYUIOP**

CPHZYOWDL instead of **ASDFGHJKL** and

FJAQTIU instead of **ZXCVBNM**

THE PILLAR MAZE:
It looks like I need to find my way through the combined maze starting at the number associated with the symbol that doesn't appear in the Wexell Cube from back at my apartment, and then cross-reference the letter it ends up at to the tools on the floor. There's also a couple of words that appear at the top!

THE CEILING MAZE:
If the letters were beaming lasers into the grid in the direction of the arrows, then the mirrors would bounce the beam around the maze to end up at another letter, theoretically at least. I just have to trace the routes!

THE STATUES:
Once I've figured out the Ceiling Maze, and what letter links to what, I should look at the Spanish names for these statues.

THE KEYPAD:
I got four numbers in Spanish from the Pillar Maze!

WEXELL'S CEO

THE CHAT WITH HENRY:
He's talking about the hall outside my apartment.

THE CEO'S KEYPAD:
Everything else in here leads to this. I just need to follow my nose, and I'll undoubtedly get some perspective.

THE STAFF HANDBOOK:
This is a code pad! So page 10, line 1, word 1 is "You", and page 10, line 1, word 2, is "should". I imagine that page 11, line 1, word 1 is "Discreet" rather than the number 2. So I just need some sets of triple numbers to start decoding. So long as they're for page 10 or 11, anyway.

THE STOCK LIST:
Like it says, I need to put the stocks in alphabetical order, making sure to keep their prices with them, and then just highlight every three in the grid!

THE FRAMED SQUARES:
I should be rolling the Wexell cube from A to B, face by face.

THE MAP OF THE WORLD:
The Spanish on here says "Map of the World" and "For cross-reference". Well, to make a cross and get a reference, I'll need four cities.

THE EMPLOYEE FILES:
Okay, some of them are employees of the month. What the devil is a worker zone, though?

THE FLOWCHART:
Everywhere I've been since discovering Henry's modifications feeds in to this. Most of the answers are just a matter of remembering what I've seen. A calm, methodical approach will unlock this, and then the boxed letters on the correct path will lead me forward.

THE REFERENCE SCHEDULE:
I suspect that one city's references will hold the key to this calendar. But which city? Three numbers every time, starting with either 10 or 11, too. Interesting.

SOLUTIONS

WELCOME TO
THE WEXELL CONSPIRACY

The lock's new code is tied to the names on the other apartments. On most of the mailboxes, certain letters in the names have been whited out:

ALISON on the top row, LISA NIXON on the second, OLIVER WILSON and FIELDING on the third.

The blanked out numbers give you three Roman numerals – I, IX, and VIII.
These correspond to 1, 9, and 8.

That gives you the numbers the lock needs to be turned to: 198.

ADAM'S APARTMENT

The door can be unlocked by revealing a code of three animals. Adam must match three names – revealed within the puzzles left by Henry in the apartment – to three animal trophies.

THE LETTER:

A keen eye will have noticed that the keys on the typewriter were in a strange order. If you decode the scrambled text of the letter by mapping a traditional QWERTY keyboard onto the typewriter, you will reveal the following message:

"I had no doubt that you would find this section of text. Well done, Adam. The code to escape can be found using the photos, then the item I left you in the post box, then the crossword mistakes. Push these three buttons in this order and you will escape."

THE PHOTOS:

You are shown a photo marked "Photos Without Them". The people in the photo - "them" - are the key to solving this puzzle.

Examining the photos on Adam's pinboard, you will notice that the people in the initial photo appear in many, but not all, of the other photos. There are five where they are not present, and these are marked with the letters E M I L Y, spelling the name Emily.

THE PUB QUIZ AND CROSSWORD:

The answers to the pub quiz questions are: Tavern, Nickname, Changeable, Obstinacy, Hard, Mixed, Curable, Democrats, Late, Fire.

Fire translates to Ignis in Latin. All of the other answers can be translated to match the Latin words in the crossword, except for Viator, Dominica, Idealismi, Degradus and Aestas.

If you take the first letters of these words, you obtain V D I D A, which is an anagram for the name David.

THE CUBE:

The sheet that Adam finds on his trophy cabinet presents you with three faces of the metallic cube, with arrows on them. Those arrows indicate which letter should be chosen when referring back to the original net from Adam's postbox. The letters are O E J, which can spell the name Joe.

THE TROPHIES:

The trophy cabinet contains the same animals as are present on the keypad, and the names Emily, David and Joe all refer to one of the animals: the butterfly, the crocodile and the sheep respectively.

The translated letter tells you the correct order to escape: Butterfly, Sheep, Crocodile

WEXELL'S RECEPTION

USERNAME:

Niki Pelling's computer still has her username visible: Niki.Pelling. Given that, we can assume the company uses a firstname.lastname style. Diane's username is therefore Diane.Llewellyn.

PASSWORD:

There are two possible ways to obtain Diane's password.

Kieran Frost is revealed to be her boyfriend by her screensaver. He is also an Employee of the Month, which tells us his start date is February 3rd, 2012.

The journal has told us that Diane has worked there for "the best part of a decade", so it is safe to assume that she would have been on reception for his first day. This provides a password (written in the American date format) of February3rd2012.

This is confirmed by following hidden information left by Kieran in the poster. One of the strange Employee of the Month quotations is emboldened and states: "A = People, B = Buildings, C = Trees and probably last; Z = Cars".

This leads to the number of objects in the poster designed by Kieran, in which there are 3 people, 2 buildings, 1 tree and 2 cars, providing a date of 3/2/12 when written in the English date format. However, when changed to the American date format it reveals itself to be 2/3/12, or February3rd2012.

SECURITY CODE:

The poster contains an exploded Sudoku hidden by Kieran in the windows. When pieced together, the Sudoku must be completed as below.

The coloured boxes thus reveal the numbers 2, 4, 7 and 9. When combined with the information about the order of Kieran's favourite colours – blue, yellow, green and red – the code is revealed to be 9427.

6	5	1	4	9	8	7	3	2
3	7	9	1	6	2	4	8	5
8	4	2	5	3	7	1	6	9
9	1	8	6	2	5	3	7	4
5	6	7	3	1	4	2	9	8
4	2	3	7	8	9	6	5	1
7	9	5	2	4	3	8	1	6
2	3	6	8	5	1	9	4	7
1	8	4	9	7	6	5	2	3

THE SECURITY OFFICE

THE PADLOCK:

Henry knocks on the wall of the cell to tell you how to find the padlock's code number. His knocks come in pairs: 3,4; 1,4; 5,5; and 2,2. These pairs of numbers are horizontal and vertical coordinates to tell you where to look on the grid of numbers above the junction boxes. The grid on the back of the chair tells you to go horizontally first, and then vertically. The number three across and four down on the grid above the boxes is 20, and the other numbers from the grid are 18, 9, and 24.

Now you have four numbers in the range of 1-26 – that is, the numeric values of four letters of the alphabet. Starting with A=1, B=2, etc, convert the numbers to letters and you have TRIX. That's the word on one of the boxes, and its voltage, which is a 3-digit value, is 930. That is the code you need to open the padlock.

THE CELL CODE:

To open the dividing cell door, you need to set each of the dials to the correct letter. The guard's paper tells you how to begin. The dotted lines on the paper are places to fold. If you fold outwards along them, the corners of the paper will point to specific numbers on the other side of the paper. Put those in order, and the four numbered folds give you the number 1950.

The letters you have available on the dials are the ones the Romans used to indicate their numbers – I, V, X, L, C, D, and M, being 1, 5, 10, 50, 100, 500, and 1000. So you need to convert 1950 to roman numerals. Roman numerals mostly ran from highest to smallest, but they had exceptions for certain numbers – 4, 9, 40, 90, 400, and 900. If you put some numerals immediately before a higher numeral, the smaller one was subtracted. So IV was 4, IX was 9, XL was 40, XC was 90, CD was 400, and CM was 900.

So converting 1950 to Roman numerals gives you MCML – 1000 + 900 + 50. Set the dials to these letters, and the door opens.

THE MAP:

The grid of letters with the colour blocks beneath it says "START HERE", and it's talking about the map. This is your gateway to understanding where to go next. As you can probably tell, the grid is a word-search, and the words you're looking for are the names on the WEXELL INSPIRES poster. Find all of those, and you'll discover that only seven letters aren't actually part of any name. Taken in order, from top left across to bottom right, they read HARWOOD.

As Henry says, when looking at the map, he needs to know where to begin. Well, you begin in the square that the word HARWOOD begins in. There are four coloured boxes beneath the word search. These colours correspond to four of the colours of the lines on the wall opposite the mirror. The lines on the wall show you which of the map's grid squares to move to, counting the large, light-coloured bricks. The small red bricks are totally passed over by the lines, which shows you not to count them.

So the red line, to start with, takes you four down and one to the left. Then the white moves you, in total, three up and four to the right. The yellow moves you four down and one to the right, and the green moves you three up and one more to the left. Either hop around the map or add those values up, and you'll find yourself moving two down and three to the right from your start – straight to LEWIS FIELD, your destination.

THE DOOR LOCK:

First, of course, you have to get out. You're looking for a five-digit number, and you know from the second keypad that it's likely some combination of 0, 0, 1, 4, and 6. The number Henry saw in his cell was 58021, which doesn't fit – and doesn't work. The grids on the guard's computer are numbered from 0 to 9 though.

Henry's number is backwards, so it should be 15082. If you take the five grids on the computer associated with those numbers, you have five cells on a five by five grid – the same five by five grid that you used to figure out the correct junction box. That translates Henry's mirror code to 13, 4, 3, 9, 22 — and converting those to letters of the alphabet like last time shows you MDCIV. That's a roman numeral for one thousand, six hundred and four. 1604. The buttons on the pad. You know that it's a 5-digit value though, and 0 is used twice. It is mathematically valid to think of 1604 as 01604 — which is the code you need to get free.

Congratulations! You're out.

THE SHED

THE TOOLS:

The way into solving this room is through the tools and the ledger recording their purchases. There are nine tools, each with an entry that lists its year of purchase, and the price paid for it. These are shown in the ledger on the bench.

Each tool also bears a rune, thus associating that rune with two separate values.

Date	Tool	Price
1964	Hatchet	£7, 2s, 6d
2004	Knife	£19.99
2009	Saw	£8.50
1998	Screwdriver	£4.49
2005	Drill	£60.00
2008	Plane	£5.99
1989	Hammer	£9.20
1980	Chisel	£8.85
2011	Scraper/filler	£45.20

THE DARTBOARD:

If you look at the dartboard, you'll realise that each of the eight darts has a different colour, and also a different value. The values of the darts are shown below.

Together, that is the information you need to gather. Now we can solve the puzzle!

Green: 60
Black: 20
Blue: 19
Red: 9
Yellow: 8
Purple: 5
White: 4
Orange: 0

THE LEGO PLATFORM:

The Lego platform has ten sets of coloured squares around it. The mat is arranged as five rows of blank 2x2 spaces with three coloured squares at each end. The colours of the squares are the same as those on the darts. If you take each set of three squares, you'll discover that it transforms into a number. The top left is Blue Green White, or 19, 60, 4. Read those three numbers to yourself, and it sounds like 1964 — the year the hatchet was purchased. In fact, all the sets of squares on the left will form years. The squares on the right have a different border, because they're not quite the same. They work in the same way — Blue Red Red is 19, 9, 9 — but it's not 1999 the year. That isn't one of the purchase years.

But it is a price, the price of the knife. The values are:

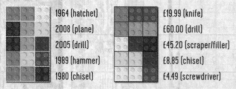

1964 (hatchet)	£19.99 (knife)
2008 (plane)	£60.00 (drill)
2005 (drill)	£45.20 (scraper/filler)
1989 (hammer)	£8.85 (chisel)
1980 (chisel)	£4.49 (screwdriver)

That means each 19-space row on the Lego platform runs from one tool to another. That doesn't help us much, but each tool has a rune, and there is a place where you can move from one rune to another and get meaningful information from it: the Rune Maze.

THE RUNE MAZE:

Cross-reference the tools with their runes, and you'll find that each date and each price has a corresponding rune in the maze. Trace the path through the maze from the rune of the year to the rune of the price for each row, and you will get a series of 19 individual numbers ranging from 1 to 5. In the same order as the decoded colours, they are as shown below:

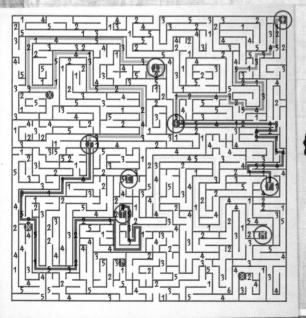

There's another place where you'll find 19 numbers, each ranging from 1 to 5: the calendar pages for January through May.

THE CALENDAR:

Now it's finally time to put the coloured Lego squares onto the platform. Run through each of the sequences of numbers. The value of the number tells you which month to look at. The position of the number in the list tells you the date. So, from top left, look at the 1st of May, the 2nd of April, the 3rd of February, the 4th of February, the 5th of January, and so on. If the day on the calendar is circled in red, assign that a red tile on the Lego mat. If it's circled in blue, assign a blue tile. So your first row from top left is starting out Red Red Red Blue Red, for example.

Once all the colours are assigned, you'll see that you have the following pattern:

THE BUNKER

Each room will give you a single-digit answer. Let's look at those first.

THE KITCHEN:

If you look at the Post-it notes on the cupboard, you'll see that most of them include the word up, down, left, or right. They're a maze. You begin with the note that begins with the word "Start", in the centre. Follow the directions listed on each note as you come to it. So from the middle note, you go "up" to "Whisk up eggs" – and up again, then right, right, down, down, left, down, left, down, left, up, left, and finally up, to the note which includes the words "correct number". The correct number for the kitchen is "2".

THE SHOWER ROOM:
The letters below each grid show you which way each one is oriented – the tops are out towards the sides of the page. If you put them the right way round and superimpose them, you get one complete grid of arrows, and one square with a circle in it, with the Latin word INITIUM at the bottom. Initium means "beginning", and it tells you your goal – find your way from the end-point, the circle, a common symbol for "off" or "stop", back to the beginning of the arrows.

So look for the arrow pointing in to the square with the circle. Move to that, and find the arrow pointing at that square. Thread on backwards, and you'll be taken through all the squares to end on row 5, column 6. Then cross-reference that starting square with the number-grid on the same page, and you'll see that the number at row 5, column 6 is "2" – the correct number for the shower room.

THE EXERCISE ROOM:
If you look at how many of each weight disk there are in the room, you'll see that there's 20×100, 8×50, 8×25, 12×10, and 15×5. Multiply those out, and you have 20×100=2000, 8×50=400, 8×25=200, 12×10=120, and 15×5=75. Sum those up so 2000+400+200+120+75=2795, and that's the total value of the weights.

To turn that value into a single digit, its digital root, add 2+7+9+5 = 23, and 2+3=5. The room's number is "5".

THE POWER ROOM:
When you follow the rules and put the wire's route together, there is only one possibility:

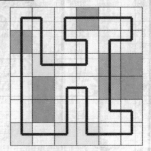

There are four unused squares, so the current – and the answer to the room – is "4".

THE REC ROOM:
If you look at the vending machine, certain item labels are out of sequence – A5 is B5, C3 is W3, and E4 is A4. That gives you three letters, BWA. Those correspond to a set of initials on the arcade machine high score table – BWA is in position 5, with a score of 50144. If you were in any doubt that position 5 was the correct answer, the digital root of 50144 is also 5+1+4+4=14 and 1+4=5. The rec room's number is "5".

THE DORM ROOM:
Once you slot the little bits of paper together, the question reads:
Solve left to right: 7 + 4 − 3 * 8 − 1 / 9 =
Well, 7 + 4 =11 − 3 =8 * 8 =64 − 1 =63 / 9 =7
The answer to the room is "7".

THE CODE:
You should have the numbers 2 for the kitchen, 2 for the showers, 5 for the exercise room, 4 for the power room, 5 for the rec room, and 7 for the dorm. Those add up to 25, the same number that is shown on the door.

The correct order to put them in is given by the panels, from left to right and top to bottom. Each panel is set in a certain orientation given by its pattern and screws. If you cross-reference the details of the cube in Chapter 1, which is where you first saw the panels, you'll find that this points you to a specific set of letters — V, M, P, S, A, and H.

Look at the map, and you'll see that the names of the rooms you can actually get into are Phoenix, Auftakt, Hunter, Shotgun, Voyageur, and Machiavelli. Cross-reference this with the panels, and you see that it's the initial letters of the rooms, in the order:

Voyageur, Machiavelli, Phoenix, Shotgun, Auftakt and Hunter.

If you follow Adam's description of his movements around the map, you'll see that he is in fact quite specific about the turnings he takes. Cross-reference the map and his findings, and you'll see that Phoenix is the kitchen, Auftakt the power room, Hunter the dorm, Shotgun the exercise room, Voyageur the rec room, and Machiavelli the shower.

You want VMPSAH, which means rec-shower-kitchen-exercise-power-dorm. So the correct order for the digits is 5-2-2-5-4-7.

Your exit code is 522547. Congratulations! You're-out.

THE UNDERWATER OFFICE

There are two primary puzzle threads you have to solve before you can finish this room. The one you encounter first is composed of the Pressure Gauge, the 4-Digit Grid, and the Filling Cups puzzles. The other comprises the Aquarium, the Water Towers, and The House of the Survivor. Once these two are complete, you can approach the Pipe Board, and finally the Grid.

The best place to start is the Filling Cups Puzzle.

FILLING CUPS PUZZLE:

This is a fairly straightforward physics puzzle. Water drips slowly through the network, obeying the laws of fluid dynamics. The task is to calculate the order that the cups will fill in, and note down the digits that each of those cups contains. There are a few tricky elements to look out for: pipes that are walled off or blocked at exit will never transmit water, and cups without a roof will overflow. If an overflowing cup is not inside another part of the network, the water will never get any further.

The first cup to fill will be the open-topped entry cup, so your first value is 6. Water will then flow into but straight out of the cup beneath it, and into a second open-topped cup with a value of 1. Initially, water will trickle off down the left pipe, into that cup. It can't go any further from there, so it will fill that one second, and your second value is 6. It'll then back up into the previous open-topped cup, and along the right-hand pipe. Before that open-topped cup is full though, the water will start flowing down into the four-junctioned central cup, worth 4, and straight through it, to the 2-cup below.

From there, the water flows into the 3-cup just to its right, and straight down to the 4-cup with two right-hand exits and one left-hand exit. All those pipes lead up above the top of the lowest 4-cup, so that will fill up next, and your third number is 4. The pipe leading left from the 4-cup is lower than the top of the open 8-cup immediately to its right, so that entire little complex of three cups that the left pipe leads to will fill next. Since the large 1-cup in that complex is taller than the two cups it leads to, the three will fill in order of the 6-cup in bottom left, the 2-cup above it, and then the large 1-cup, so your next three numbers are 6, 2, and

1. Then the level in the pipes leading right (and up) from the lowest 4-cup can rise. As it does, it will fill the open-topped 8-cup next, giving you an 8.

This cup isn't spilling into the network, it's spilling outside it. The water will never rise higher. That means, in order, that the answer to the Filling Cups is 6, 6, 4, 6, 2, 1, and 8 – or 6646218.

PRESSURE GAUGE:

Moving back to the pressure gauge, if you look at the image closely, you'll notice that some of the numbers on the dial have been replaced with letters. The inner scale reads 2, 4, 6, V, 10, 1L, 1C, 1M, and the outer one reads 0, 50, X00, 150, 200. From the numbers that are present, it's clear that the gauge is linear, so you can deduce readily that:

| V | = | 8 | L | = | 2 | C | = | 4 |
| M | = | 6 | X | = | 1 | | | |

These letters are all Roman numerals, although the gauge does not assign them their usual values. But those values are precisely those of the digits of the number you got from the Filling Cups puzzle.

Replace the digits of your 7-digit cup number with the letters shown on the gauge, and you'll turn 6646218 into MMCMLXV. That's a correct Roman number. MM is 2,000, CM is 900, LX is 60, and V is 5, which gives you 2965. Far more useful!

4-DIGIT GRID:

Once you have your 4-digit number from the gauge, this is the place to turn. Apart from the number you already have, 2965, the other numbers are completely random. What you need to know is the location in the 6x6 pattern that 2965 corresponds to – square F5, or the one directly above bottom right. Keep a note of that, because you'll need it later.

WATER TOWERS:

Now we're starting on the other part of the process. The water towers are, in effect, a maze, where each route you take between towers gives you a letter towards spelling out a word. You know the entry and exit points – the 10-high tower and the 0-high tower respectively – and you know that you can only go from one tower to another tower that is exactly one level lower. So your route has to be 10-9-8-7-6-5-4-3-2-1-0.

There's only one trail that works. From the top 10-tower, directly below top left, go north-east (S) to 9, south-east (K) to 8, south-east (I) to 7, south-east (N) to 6, north-east (N) to 5, south-east (Y) to 4, south-west (F) to 3, south-west (I) to 2, south-east (S) to 1, and south-east (H) to 0.

That spells out SKINNYFISH.

AQUARIUM:

Skinnyfish are mentioned in the context of the aquarium. If you look at the list, you'll see that the tank is kept at 1 grey cat fish, 1 blue doublefish, 1 pink shrimp, 1 bronzefish, 1 red flattyfish, 3 yellow dollyfish, 1 black toad, 1 green dogfish, 7 silver skinnyfish and 1 white ghostfish. It also has a red treasure chest, a brown log, an orange bridge, a black cave, a blue castle, cream stones, green bamboo, some moss and some fern inside.

The instruction tells you to add a fish – thanks to the water towers, we know that the extra fish is a skinnyfish. We've seen the Wexell magazine spread on fish habits before, in Chapter 2 in fact. Turn back to that and you'll see that the various fish all react in certain ways according to specific triggers. Follow the logic through, and you'll see that if you did have a skinnyfish to add, this is how it would all play out:

Round 0. Add 1 silver skinnyfish. That leaves 19 creatures in total.

Round 1. The black toad is overcrowded, and leaves the aquarium with the bamboo. 18 remain.

Round 2. Without the toad present, the pink shrimp hides under the brown log, and since the bamboo is gone, the bronzefish eats all the fern. Still 18 remain.

Round 3. There's no fern left, so the bronzefish hides in the black cave, and the grey catfish gets violent and smashes the brown log, killing the pink shrimp. 17 remain.

Round 4. The green dogfish eats the dead shrimp, and dies. The white ghostfish sees this poisoning, and clouds up the water. 16 remain.

Round 5. The blue doublefish can't see, so enters the blue castle feeling violent. Still 16 remain.

Round 6. When the water starts clearing, the white ghostfish seeks shelter in the blue castle, and is eaten by the blue doublefish. 15 remain.

At this point, our survivors are 1 grey catfish, 1 blue doublefish, 1 bronzefish, 1 red flattyfish, 3 yellow dollyfish, and 8 silver skinnyfish.

Round 7. The silver skinnyfish now make up more than half the population, and immediately eat all the yellow dollyfish. 12 remain.

Round 8. With no yellow dollyfish to suppress it, the red flattyfish hulks out and kills all the silver skinnyfish as well as the blue doublefish. Just 3 now survive. The red flattyfish, the grey catfish, and the bronzefish.

Round 9. With just three species of fish still in the tank, the grey catfish eats the red flattyfish. 2 remain.

Round 10. The grey catfish, which can now not see the bronzefish in its cave, dies because it is scared of being alone.

Just 1 fish is left, and the survivor is the bronzefish – whose "house" is the black cave.

THE HOUSE OF THE SURVIVOR:

Now it's time to tackle the House of the Survivor. If you have the facilities and the technical know-how, you can set up a grid of hexagonal cells on a computer, and colour them as they are in the diagram as preparation. If not, you'll have to join the rest of us in using notepaper, staggered columns of circles, and letter abbreviations for each colour.

The instructions are in the letter with the menacing Post-it note, and they tell you everything you need to know to approach this puzzle. You start by removing one colour.

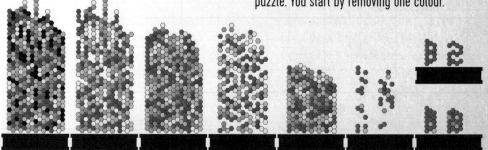

That colour is the same colour as the house of the survivor from the fish-tank — that is, black. Remove all the black cells, and then each column settles down to use up all the empty spaces. Once you've done that, identify each place in the resulting diagram where a there's cluster of three or more cells — that is, a group where each one borders at least one other of the same colour. Remove all these clusters, and settle again.

After the fourth round of culls, you're left with two small packs of cells separated by white space. Each group is dominated by blue, and if you ignore the remaining singleton colours, you'll clearly see that the two groups say "B2".

PIPES:

Like F5 earlier, B2 is a reference for a square on the 6x6 grid of numbers. The board for the pipes is also a 6x6 grid, and to begin solving the pipes, you need to know where your pipeline starts and finishes. That's what B2 and F5 are — the pipe's termini.

Therefore, we know that the pipe runs from the square one space diagonally in from top left to the square immediately above bottom right. The pipe pieces shown in the puzzle tell you what you have to work with.

The important thing to note is that you have 12 pieces — the two termini, three corner segments, and seven straight sections. The limited number of corner segments means that you can only make three turns. The B2 terminus can only run one square in any direction before needing a turn, so you have two more corner segments available.

The F5 terminus can either go up to a bundle of fixed pipes that it would take three turns to navigate — impossible with what you have — or

straight down, requiring an immediate turn. It has to be the latter, and that means you have only one corner segment left.

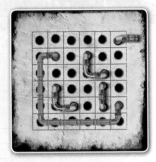

There's only remaining route between F5 pointing downwards and a square next to B2 that takes only one turn, and that's along the outside edge of the square. When you put in the termini and all three corner segments, you have seven empty spaces along the route round the outside — and seven straight pipes. So the answer is:

B2-A2-A3-A4-A5-A6-B6-C6-D6-E6-F6-F5.

THE GRID:

The last step is very straight-forward. You now have a pattern of twelve points on a 6x6 board (the pipes), and you need a pattern of twelve points on a different 6x6 board (the grid). Put the pipe layout into the grid.

Congratulations! You're out.

THE SERVER ROOM

THE WIRE PANEL:

The first part of this room is fully self-contained. You have a number of symbols on a plug-board, a set of diagrams linking two symbols together, and a table of designs that translate to certain letters. If you take a moment to look at the pairs of linked symbols, you'll see that the pairs of ports they represent are all adjacent, and that gives you the way forward here.

Connect each pair of ports in the list, and you'll come up with three distinct shapes on the board

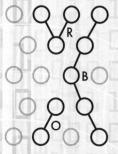

– a short diagonal line, a v-shape, and a tall chevron. The instructions say to translate from the shortest symbol. With just one stretch of wire, that's the diagonal line. Look up in the table, and you'll see it's an O.

The next shape, with two wires, is the v-shape. It translates to R. Finally the chevron pointing left, with four wires, gives you a B.

The answer is ORB.

THE SERVER STACKS:

Moving into the larger server room, there are several issues to take on board. Aside from the keyboard, you have four stacks, and each one has a 3x3 grid on top of it. The stacks rotate, and as the far left stack says on one side, you have to ensure a particular total of LEDs are facing south. So each stack has to be rotated to have the correct side facing south – the direction you entered the room from, as EROS told you.

Your first task is to work out which side for each stack should be facing south.

THE BINARY STACK:

There are four panels each holding eight binary numbers – base 2, that is. In binary, every digit is either 0 or 1, the right-hand column of digits represents 1, and moving leftwards, each column is worth twice as much as the previous.

A 1 in a column means that you add that column's value to the number's total, and 0 means that you don't. So in binary:

01 is zero+one=1,

10 is two+zero=2, and

11 is two+one=3.

The binary numbers on the stack are all five digits long, which means the columns are worth:

16	8	4	2	1

The maximum you can get to with a five-digit binary number is 11111, which means 16+8+4+2+1, and comes to 31.

If you work out the decimal numbers shown on each panel, you'll see that they work out to:

25-17-7-11-9-24-4-18, 22-15-25-1-7-5-21-18, 5-21-25-12-17-11-11-25, and 17-2-1-10-19-24-7-18

The thing to notice here is that none of the numbers is more than 26. That should clue you in to the possibility of an alphabetic cipher. The simplest alphabetic number cipher is where A=1, B=2, etc. Try that, and you'll find that the numbers on the panels translate to:

YQGKIXDR; VOYAGEUR; EUYLQKKY; QBAJSXGR

VOYAGEUR is the name of the project, and therefore the important panel is the one with two white LEDs and two red LEDs. This is the side that should face south.

THE NONOGRAM STACK:

You can't do much with the second stack Adam mentions just yet, so skip over it to the Nonogram. This is a fairly straight-forward type of puzzle. The way to approach solving it is to start by looking at the larger numbers in the design. Look at the furthest position in the row or column where the row of boxes could start and still fit in, and compare it with the nearest position where the row could end. If there's overlap – any time the row is longer than half of the grid – then those overlap squares must be shaded. Then cross-reference those squares with the other axis. If there's just one number on the other axis, then that group of cells has to include the shaded cell, which will give you limits to work from, and some cells that must be unshaded. Keep at it, and it'll all fall into place, giving you:

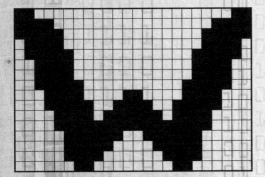

When you assemble the Nonogram design from the cut-out it is clear that one panel of the Nonogram stack is "original South" – that is, the southwards orientation for the stack as it originally rises from the floor. The solved Nonogram tells you that W, short for west, is the stack's solution. So if the side with two yellow and two white LEDs is the south face, the west face is the next face if you turn it anti-clockwise: the face with three white LEDs and one yellow LED. This is the side that should face south.

THE MOTHERBOARD STACK:

The task for the final stack is to place the correct circuit into each motherboard so that each of the four lines correctly runs from top to bottom, A to A, B to B, etc. Pick a motherboard, and a line, and see where it finishes at the end of the top section, and then work back at the lower part to see where the same line begins at the start of the bottom section.

The A-line of the first motherboard, for example, finishes the top section in channel

C, and starts the bottom section in channel D, so the correct circuit for that motherboard has a connection running from channel C to channel D. There are two possibilities, the top and bottom circuits. Next, look at the B-line for the same motherboard – B is a straight through connection, so you need a circuit with a B to B connection. That's the top one, the only possibility.

Proceed in this manner, and you'll discover that the third motherboard is the one that takes the circuit marked SOUTH. Cross-reference the cut-outs, and you can see that this motherboard is beneath one white LED, two green LEDs, and one blue LED. This is the side that should face south.

THE LED VIEW STACK:

Once you have the other three stacks correctly orientated, the text on the second stack becomes useful. It says "Ensure 2 green, 4 yellow, 2 red, 2 blue from the South before merge". Looking at the LEDs you have facing south so far, you have 2 green, 1 yellow, 2 red, and 1 blue. So to make up the right total, you need this remaining stack to have a south-facing side with 3 yellow LEDs and 1 blue LED.

THE SOUTH GRIDS:

Now you know which way each of the four stacks has to face. You also know where the stacks are compared to one another. EROS tells you to "proceed northwards" into the main room, so you're entering from the south. This means the bottom left corner of your square of stacks is the Binary Stack, bottom right is the Motherboard Stack, top left is the LED View Stack, and top right is the Nonogram Stack.

As indicated by the floor and the text on the LED View Stack, you need to bring these four stacks together when they're in their correct orientations.

You don't have to cut out the designs, but if you do, it might be easier for you to ensure each of the 3x3 grids on top of the stacks are in the correct position. Whether you cut them out or not, when you bring them together, you get the following pattern:

From what EROS tells you, you know that you are looking for a six-digit code that totals 24, where the digits are separated by emptiness. The South Grids combined have 24 black squares.

At first glance, the sequences of black squares appear to be broken up into nine segments, not six. But the things dividing the sequences are blank spaces – emptiness. The trick is to not stop counting at the end of a row, but instead continue immediately from the left side of the next row down, just as if you were counting the number of words in a sentence on a page.

Then the black squares are broken up in six groups – 4, 5, 3, 6, 2 and 4 – giving you six digits that total 24.

THE KEYPAD:

All that remains is to enter the code 453624 into the keypad.

Congratulations! You're out.

THE LIBRARY

THE MANUSCRIPT:

The heart of this chapter is contained within the genealogical manuscript. We'll come back to the details of the text in a little while, but first, I want you to notice that when the manuscript is held up to the light, you can see a lion and a number – two – hidden in the illustration.

That's the key to beginning the process of unlocking this chapter.

THE VINTAGE SCALES:

Now look forward a little. The vintage weighing scales give you a set of equivalences, balancing various heraldic design elements against each other. At the bottom right, we see that a lion is equivalent to two swords.

So two lions, as on the manuscript, equals four swords. Directly above it, we can see that four swords (or two lions) is worth one dragon, and to the left, a dragon is worth two swords and three crowns (and since two swords are worth half a dragon, three crowns must be the same as two swords, or one lion).

So working through, two lions would be worth four swords, one dragon, or six crowns.

THE COATS OF ARMS:

Turning back to the heraldic coats of arms, you will see that all four of the designs are made up of various numbers of lions, dragons, crowns and swords. There are also wolves on two of the crests, but as these aren't on all of them or on the scales, they can be discounted. We already have some numbers of elements set up via the balances, and two coat of arms fit the balance set out in the vintage scales: Lopez and Perez. However, only one of these has just two lions, as indicated in the manuscript, with six crowns, four swords, two lions, and one dragon – the house of Lopez.

Lopez

THE TEXT MESSAGES:

As Adam notes, one of the messages stood out. Each of the numbers has 7 digits, but they're not broken up in the same way, and each break in the digits leaves you a number less than 27. Convert the phone numbers to letters by their position in the alphabet, as in EROS's previous puzzle, and you'll immediately see that 5-18-15-19 spells out EROS. She's sent a well-disguised clue. In the text, she mentions "your house" – the house you've already identified, the house of Lopez, and takes pains to draw your attention to the second youngest area network.

Between the coat of arms and EROS's text, you have a clear objective: the second youngest member of the house of Lopez.

THE FAMILY TREE:

The genealogy presented in the manuscript is very detailed, and if you work through it person by person, you'll very quickly discover that it fits the family tree diagram perfectly. So your task is to fill in the tree, working your way down to the two youngest members of the Lopez family.

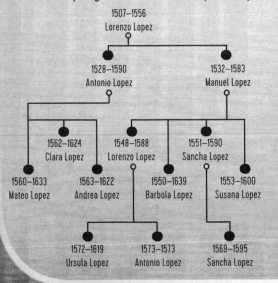

So from the people listed in the text, the youngest Lopez is Antonio (b.1573), and the second youngest is Ursula, who was born in 1572 and died in 1619.

THE CRACKED MOBILE PHONE:

Under the manuscript, a cracked mobile phone specifies spaces for years of birth and death, and each digit has a colour. Three of the digits are red, and the rest are all different. Now look at the digits of Ursula's dates of birth and death. They are all different, apart from three 1s, which are in the same relative position as the red Ys on the phone.

From that, we can be confident that red=1, yellow=2, white=5, blue=6, green=7 and pink=9.

THE OLD COMPUTER:

Now we know that some colours have numeric value here, we can turn to the old computer, with its enigmatic patterns. The first line, red white × pink = orange, tells us that orange is worth 15×9, or 135. The second line, blue + yellow = grey, tells us that grey is worth 6+2, or 8.

The next line is more complicated, but we have all the pieces now. From (orange + red)/grey, we can get (135+1)/8, and 136/8=17. Blue+green is simple, 6+7=13. Multiply these pieces, and 17×13=221. Now we have two last values to subtract, 7 and 9. 221-7-9 gives us 205, Adam's apartment number.

THE KEYPAD:

Henry was there first, and he confirms it: the exit code is meaningful to Adam. 205. His apartment number.

Congratulations! You're out.

THE ANCIENT RUIN

THE STICK-UP:

This chapter brings you to a screeching halt almost immediately with the Stick-Up. Henry's trying to help, but the key to working out what he means is in his choice of words — "type up a good story about this, back in your apartment."

Adam was in his apartment in Chapter One, where Henry had tampered with his typewriter by switching the labels on all the keys, creating a code. If you refer back to that chapter, you'll see that the "I" label is on the 'N'-key. So you know that 'I' decodes to 'N'.

Follow through the whole of 'In snack', and you'll quickly see that it's code for 'No tocar' — the sign on the door, and your hint for a way forward.

THE PILLAR MAZE:

The heart of this chapter is the pillar maze. It's split into two parts, and first you have to reassemble it by folding the pages over so they overlap properly (or by copying and printing those sections out). Once it's back in one piece, the first thing you'll notice is that the designs along the edge spell out "dos cuatro". Set that aside for now.

The two bronze plates, set next to each other, spell out "EXTRAÑO UNO". This literally means "strange one", and is listed on the archaeologist's notebook as meaning "odd one out." Above the left half of the maze are numbers and symbols. If you refer back to the now-familiar list of Wexell symbols that appear on the cube you first met in Chapter One, you'll see that all but one of the maze's seven symbols are from the cube. The remaining one is a simple equal-armed cross, and it is number 3.

Start at number 3 in the maze, and follow the paths. Only one of them leads to another alphanumeric — specifically, the letter A. Above

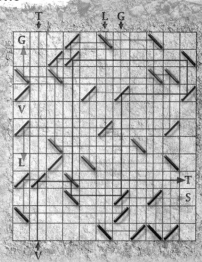

the right-hand side of the maze, the letter A is associated with the symbol of a chisel. If you turn to the labelled tools, you'll find that one of them is indeed a chisel, and the label that holds the same symbol also holds the word "seisocho". Make a note of that too, and the Pillar Maze is defeated.

THE CEILING MAZE:

Working from the archaeologist's sketch, you'll see that each of the letters around the edge is an entry to the grid. Imagine you were shining a beam of light from each letter, and it reflected perfectly at each mirror. Then with a bit of bouncing around, you'll see that V goes to T, T goes to L, L goes to G, and G goes to S.

THE STATUES:

In order to get the statues in the correct alignment, you need to think about their names — specifically, their names in Spanish. Watcher is Vigilante. Traitor is Traidor. Leader is Lider. Warrior is Guerrero. Dreamer is Soñador. Their initials are V, T, L, G and S.

These are the linkages you got from the Ceiling Maze. Point the watcher at the traitor, the traitor at the leader, the leader at the warrior, and the warrior at the dreamer, and the keypad will arise.

THE KEYPAD:

Finally, you need to put four numbers into the keypad. When you put the pillar maze together, you get "dos cuatro", and when you identify the chisel tool, you get "seis ocho". Compare this to the Spanish in the archaeologist's notebook, and you'll immediately see that these translate to two, four, six, and eight. Put those into the keypad.

Congratulations! You're out.

WEXELL'S CEO

THE CHAT WITH HENRY:

This is just a simple little teaser puzzle, a warm-up to the main course. In Chapter 1, Adam's post box label has some eroded letters – his surname is Parkinson, but the "kin" is missing, so it looks a bit like Adam Par Son. Missing "kin", sending "post" – Henry's reminding Adam of a small personal detail in his own quirky style.

That's all there is to it.

Moving forward, there are eight further challenges waiting for you in this chapter. Half of them stand alone, and can be addressed in any order. The other half work together in a specific sequence, drawing on the solutions to the first four. We'll look at them in the order they appear in the book, for sake of simplicity.

THE STOCK LIST:

The key thing to take from the list of stocks and shares is the heading on the blank side of the paper: "Alphabetical – Mark 3s", also called out specifically in the text. This is your instruction on how to solve the problem. You simply need to put the stocks and their values in alphabetical order first:

ALPHABETICAL – MARK 3S

	HIGH	LOW	CLOSE	
ABBEY	4 3 2 1 3 0	4 6 2 1 2 0	4 6 2 1 5 2	↑
ACORN	5 3 0 0 3 1	5 2 9 9 7 9	5 2 9 9 8 2	↑
BRAVE	2 3 3 3 3 4	2 2 9 9 9 9	2 2 9 7 6 8	↓
CALVON	5 3 0 0 3 7	5 2 9 7 5 6	5 2 9 6 4 5	↓
DELFIN	4 3 0 1 3 2	3 3 9 6 4 7	4 4 1 0 2 6	↑
DISHONE	7 6 4 2 1 3	7 6 3 8 8 4	7 6 4 4 8 0	↑
ELFIX	6 5 5 9 8 3	6 5 3 9 7 7	6 5 5 0 9 9	↑
FORTY	4 7 0 1 2 0	3 3 9 8 8 8	4 7 0 1 5 2	↑
GAINWAY	2 9 9 8 7 7	2 9 9 3 6 5	3 0 1 5 4 1	↑
HOPPA	4 0 0 8 1 6	4 0 0 3 3 9	3 9 7 8 8 2	↓
IBEX	2 8 8 9 9 5	2 8 7 3 4 3	3 0 2 7 6 6	↑
JAYWAY	4 1 5 2 6 6	4 0 9 3 5 6	3 9 3 3 7 5	↓
JOLLY	1 4 7 5 2 7	1 4 7 5 1 4	1 3 9 8 2 7	↓
KISS	8 4 3 7 5 3	8 4 2 9 6 0	8 3 8 3 3 9	↓
LAYLOW	1 6 3 3 3 0	1 6 2 7 4 1	1 6 3 3 7 2	↑
LOTZOV	5 2 3 6 3 6	5 2 1 0 0 2	5 2 7 0 4 4	↑
LEMING	6 0 3 1 1 3	6 0 2 9 1 7	6 0 2 8 9 6	↓
MATRIX	5 0 9 0 1 0	5 0 8 7 9 2	5 0 8 7 7 7	↓
NINNON	4 0 0 0 5 3	3 9 9 8 7 4	4 0 1 1 2 7	↑
NEWBY	1 4 6 4 3 5	1 3 9 0 2 5	1 4 6 5 0 0	↑
OPENS	8 4 0 0 0 3	8 3 9 7 2 5	1 8 4 1 0 5	↓
POLIMAR	4 0 0 6 7 3	3 9 9 4 8 7	4 0 1 2 0 6	↑
QUEST	9 1 9 1 1 1	9 1 9 1 0 1	9 1 9 1 8 5	↑
READY	4 0 5 0 2 6	3 8 8 3 7 7	4 0 5 1 7 6	↑
STEADY	4 1 2 8 7 7	3 3 6 3 9 6	4 1 4 0 4 0	↑
TOPPO	4 0 0 6 5 5	3 7 3 3 9 8	4 0 0 7 0 6	↑
TANGO	4 1 1 0 0 0	3 9 8 3 7 2	4 3 9 0 6 5 7	↑
UNICORN	2 9 0 4 6 6	2 8 7 5 4 3	3 0 0 0 0 1	↓
UPPA	5 7 1 8 7 5	5 7 1 0 3 9	5 7 0 6 4 8	↓
VICTOR	4 1 6 2 5 0	4 0 8 6 3 0	3 3 9 7 7 5	↓
WEXELL	2 8 9 6 7 6	2 8 6 9 7 3	3 0 5 0 0 6	↑

And then highlight the 3s:

ALPHABETICAL – MARK 3S

	HIGH	LOW	CLOSE
ABBEY	3 3		
ACORN	3 3		
BRAVE	3 3 3 3		
CALVON	3 3		
DELFIN	3 3	3 3	
DISHONE		3 3	
ELFIX		3 3	
FORTY		3 3	
GAINWAY		3	3
HOPPA		3 3	3
IBEX		3	3 3
JAYWAY		3	3 3 3
JOLLY			3
KISS	3 3		3 3
LAYLOW	3 3 3		3 3
LOTZOV	3 3		
LEMING	3 3		
MATRIX			
NINNON		3 3	
NEWBY	3	3	
OPENS	3	3	
POLIMAR		3 3	
QUEST			
READY		3 3	
STEADY		3 3 3	
TOPPO		3 3 3	
TANGO		3	
UNICORN			3 3
UPPA		3	
VICTOR		3	3 3
WEXELL			3 3

The 3s clearly spell out "Hong Kong". Make a note, and move on to the next puzzle.

THE FRAMED SQUARES:

You've seen the Wexell symbol/letter cube from Chapter 1 several times now. This is its final outing. Each picture contains a square with a letter. Arrange the cube — or, if you're great with spatial manipulation in your head, imagine it — so that the letter from the picture is in the same position in front of you.

So, if the picture has an S upright on the top edge, arrange the cube so that the face with a symbol a bit like a box containing an H with an extended centre bar is upright, and the S is at the top.

Once it's aligned correctly, roll the cube through the pattern that the empty black and white squares show in the picture, and check the letter in the ? position at the end of the trail.

Specifically:
For the picture containing P, roll the cube to the right, then up, up, up, and check the left-hand edge to get "N".

From R, roll up, up, left, left, and check left-hand edge for "U".

From either D on the cube, roll down, down, down, down, and check upper edge to get back to the same "D".

From N, roll left, up, up, up, left, and check top edge for "A".

From T, roll left, up, up, up, right, right, down, and check right edge for "K".

From S, roll right, down, down, down, down, and check lower edge for "L".

From I, roll up, left, left, down and check lower edge for "A".

From W, roll up, up, left, left, down and check lower edge for "C".

That gives you NUDAKLAC. That's an anagram for another city: "Auckland". Again, make a note and move on.

THE EMPLOYEE FILES:

The files show you a selection of outstanding employees for "board consideration" — the board in question being the Employee of the Month board, which you saw in Chapter 2.

Eight of the faces here match people from the Employee of the Month board — Charlie Bond, Helen Chris, Rohin Dale, Judi Effie, Richard Horton, Emma Kendrick, Christina Mitchell, and Ellen Williams. All the employees have a Worker zone assignment, and if you look at featured employees' zones, you see that in order, they are S, A, N, T, I, A, G and O. That's a third city, "Santiago".

THE FLOWCHART:

This puzzle tests you on how you did in previous chapters. If you skipped any, you're likely to be stuck! Let's look at the answers.

1. **Auftakt is South of Blinds**. That's from the layout of the bunker from chapter 5, and no, once you work out where everything is, Auftakt is east of blinds. False. Take an "A".

2. **Jose Garcia was born exactly 100yrs after his great-great-grandfather**. That's the family tree from the Library in Chapter 8. Jose Garcia was born 93yrs after his great-great-grandfather. False. "C".

3. **4y 3g 4b = North**. That's from EROS's rotating stacks from the Server Room, Chapter 7. Once everything is set up correctly, there are 5 yellow, 3 green, and 4 blue lights facing north. False. "V".

4. **Total tool value = £168.22 +2s +2d**. The tools and their prices were in the Shed, Chapter 4. Add them up, and you'll find they come to £169.22 +2s +2d. False again. "V".

5. KRAN=940v. KRAN is one of the electricity boxes on the wall of the Security Office in Chapter 3. It's labelled 920v. False. "E".

6. Emily is a butterfly. Emily is one of the figurines that Adam has in his apartment in Chapter 1. She is indeed a butterfly. True. "N".

7. Glasses=May. On the Employee of the Month board in Chapter 2, there aren't any Employee names, but the person selected for May is indeed wearing glasses. True. "U".

8. VLCMX=82461. This refers to the water valve in Chapter 6 which has had some numbers replaced with letters. Cross-check, and you'll see that V replaces 8, L is 2, C is 4, M is 6, and X is 1. True. "O".

9. The symbol with two overlapping crescents = DUOSEIS. From the pillars of the Ancient Ruin in Chapter 9, we know that symbol is marked as "6". The Spanish for six is seis, not duoseis, and "duo" means the same in Spanish as it does in English (although in Spanish, the U has an accent). False. "R".

So that gives you A C V V E N U O R, which is an anagram of "Vancouver", your fourth city.

THE MAP OF THE WORLD:
Now that you have four cities, it's time to turn to the map of the world — the Mapa del Mundo — hanging on the wall. Vancouver and Santiago are towards the left edge, Auckland and Hong Kong towards the right. The bottom of the map says "Por referencia cruzada" — which is Spanish for "For cross-reference". Cross your references, Hong Kong to Santiago, and Auckland to Vancouver.

The place they cross is Nairobi.

THE REFERENCE SCHEDULE:
There's one other place in this chapter where Nairobi is mentioned — on the reference schedule calendar of meetings and calls. Examine the calendar, and you'll find that there are three meetings that mention Nairobi:

Sept 22, 10am, 9 Accra Rd, 3 people

Sept 23, 11am, 7th train line, 6 people

Sept 24, 10am – 6pm, 2nd full day.

That's all you need from here.

THE STAFF HANDBOOK:
The Post-it note on the staff handbook says "Critical for meetings", and indeed, this is where you make sense of the meetings that mention Nairobi. Each of the meetings on the calendar first mentions either 10am or 11am. That's the detail that confirms for you that each entry is a reference to either p10 or p11 of the handbook.

So each of the references has three numbers. In a typical book code — like this one — the numbers tell you page, line, and word. Looking at the Nairobi data from the schedule, you have 10 – 9 – 3, 11 – 7 – 6, and 10 – 6 – 2.

Look up those words in turn. Page 10, line 9, word 3 is "up". Page 11, line 7, word 7 is "side". Finally, page 10, line 6, word 2 is "down".

Up side down.

And what does that mean? Well, look at the Post-it note again. It finishes with "see CEO." So let's do that.

THE CEO'S KEYPAD:
The staff handbook directs you to see the CEO upside-down. Do that, and you should quickly notice that the artist's signature in the bottom left corner of the CEO's picture is actually a set of six digits:

371605.

All that remains is to thump them into the keypad.

Congratulations! You're out.

BONUS SOLUTION

Did you notice the Morse code throughout the book? Look for the triangles... they gave you hints if you were observant enough.

CREDITS

The publishers would like to thank the following sources for their kind permission to reproduce the pictures in this book: